Medicine and Gasoline
On the Road in America with Lucky Boys Confusion

Revised Edition
With a new Afterword by the author

Jason, Ryan, Stubhy, Joe, Adam: Lucky Boys Confusion, 2006. (photo: Nabil Elderkin)

By
Derek Brezette

Foreword by Stubhy Pandav

Cover Design: Bill Carreon

BannedCast.com

Copyright © 2007 by Derek Brezette

ISBN 978-0-7414-4163-8

Printed in the United States of America

Published November 2012

INFINITY PUBLISHING
1094 New DeHaven Street, Suite 100
West Conshohocken, PA 19428-2713
Toll-free (877) BUY BOOK
Local Phone (610) 941-9999
Fax (610) 941-9959
Info@buybooksontheweb.com
www.buybooksontheweb.com

"Who are *you*?" said the Caterpillar.

"I—I hardly know, sir, just at present—at least I know who I *was* when I got up this morning, but I think I must have been changed several times since then."

"What do you mean by that?" said the Caterpillar sternly. "Explain yourself!"

"I can't explain *myself*, I'm afraid, sir," said Alice, "because I'm not myself, you see."

"I don't see," said the Caterpillar.

"I'm afraid I can't put it more clearly," Alice replied very politely, "for I can't understand it myself to begin with; and being so many different sizes in a day is very confusing."

Lewis Carroll
Alice's Adventures in Wonderland

Lucky Boys Confusion: Hopeless Dreamers
Reggae Hip-hop Punk Rock Stylee!

Early Lucky Boys Confusion Flyer

DISCLAIMER

Most disclaimers are brief implorations unto the reader to understand that names and places within the following text have been changed for legal reasons. While many names and places in this book *have* been changed for legal reasons, I feel it necessary to take a moment to further discuss the nature and veracity of the text that follows.

What I have done in this book is combine elements of fiction with elements of nonfiction in order to distort the worlds of both. The line between fact and fiction is most blurred in the five 'city-stories' that follow, while the interviews and segments that document the band's history are, to the best of my ability, indisputably accurate.

The band members' characters in the city-stories admittedly resemble rock n' roll caricatures more than fastidiously accurate documentarian accounts. This does not stray from the tradition of rock n' roll mythmaking and should not make the stories and their characters any less plausible, and certainly no less probable.

In my defense I would argue that this occasional blurring of fact and fiction is nothing new to American letters, and I have only pirated the motif for practical purposes.

John Smith, who produced some of America's earliest writings, might also have produced the earliest example of what is known today as creative nonfiction when he wrote about the events surrounding the settlement of Jamestown colony. It is rather remarkable, for instance, that John Smith, writing several years after the events and in the comforts of England, would be able to recall with such precision the discourses between himself and chief Powhatan. Even more remarkable is the eloquence with which Powhatan, in his sixties when he meets his first Englishman, speaks with John Smith. Perhaps the chieftain had purchased early copies of Rosetta Stone company's English instructional tapes or was invested with a remarkable linguistic ability heretofore unparalleled in any time or place. Or perhaps—and prepare yourself for a shock—John Smith fabricated most of Powhatan's dialogues.

I'll concede that it is entirely possible that at one point Powhatan said something akin to, "some doubt I have of your coming hither, that makes me not so kindly seek to relieve you as I would," as John Smith records Powhatan as having said, but I have some doubts. It is equally likely that John Smith may have chanced to express himself in Powhatan's native language, just as there is always the possibility that a room full of chimps sitting at typewriters will produce a copy of *Harry Potter and the Sorcerer's Stone* or, at the very least, *Hamlet*.

We might also look to Christopher Columbus's journal entries, whose imperialist depictions of the Native Americans he finds in the Caribbean indicates less about the Native Americans he encountered than it does about Columbus and his intended audience's desires—that of the king and queen of Spain. Thus the repeated references to gold and a potential crop of trainable slave labor with "well-formed bodies" and hair resembling "horse-hair." While we tend to view these examples with an air of dismissive judgment because our own prevailing moral sensibilities now disdain such imperialist disregard for foreign cultures, we turn a blind eye to our own propensity to construct and consume narratives composed of equally suggestive rhetorical flourishes. This blindness, combined with our subsequent susceptibility to those influences, is what contemporary advertisers prey upon.

The point is that narratives always behave as representations, and to ingest them as anything else is always a mistake. This makes narratives no less valuable nor divests them of merit, but merely cautions one against reading what is not present while ignoring what is. What *is* present is a presentation set forth by an author, a message for a reader—some (both readers and authors) better than others. And meaning is the responsibility of each: the author to articulate it, the reader to decipher it and decide upon its merit, or lack thereof.

Welcome to the show.

Commitment

A Foreword by Stubhy Pandav

"Hey man, tell me, you do this for the chicks, right?"
"So, shots on you tonight, rockstar?"
"Out of all the cars you own, which one's your favorite?"
"Man, you've got the life: young, rich and famous."

Random drunk fans

Summer, 2006.

Earlier this year the band and I went up to Minnesota to give it another shot and recorded an EP with Matt Kirkwood that we intended to use to shop for a new label. We were excited when we got the final product back and thought that we were on our way again. After we shopped the album and we saw that no one was going to bite, I came to the realization that no matter what kind of song Adam and I wrote, any song with the stamp of Lucky Boys Confusion was never going to receive a fair shot again. Things like that are hard to digest after so many years of effort.

Despite myself, when the band was offered a distribution deal with Reincarnate Music, I jumped at it. I can't remember exactly what was going through my head when we came to this decision; most of my memories of LBC are blurry feelings of barreling forward head first and not looking back.

May, 2006. Beat Kitchen. Chicago. Lucky Boys Confusion's Five Night Stand. All Nights Sold Out.

Our EP *How to Get Out Alive* has charted on the Billboard Heatseekers Chart and has sold approx 1,300 copies in its first week of release. For Indie standards, these are great numbers. Major labels would laugh. The five night stand made us close to $15,000.

Next 2 /12 Months. Get Happy Tour with Bowling for Soup.

Any unsigned band should be more than excited to receive this opportunity to tour with an established act. But something was missing. It was ironic that the tour was called "Get Happy," because outside of alcohol, I could find nothing that made me feel good about what I was doing. I was very depressed and unsatisfied and so ashamed that I felt this way. I knew there were so many bands that would kill for this opportunity, but it just didn't matter. I couldn't get out of this funk.

I guess that's what people mean when they say reality is sinking in, but I disagree with that cliché. When a person and their reality come face to face I don't think it has anything to do with "sinking in," I think it has everything to do with reality pulling back and slapping you in the face over and over again until that feeling just becomes part your daily routine.

After a month and a half of touring, we finally had a meltdown one morning on our way to the next town. That's all I really want to say about that morning because the details aren't anyone's fucking business. That'll stay between me and my four boys and anyone that we choose to tell.

This story isn't special because it's about Lucky Boys Confusion, this story's special because it captures what so many mid to low-level bands are going through everyday. I think Derek really captured that part of what we were going through. He grew up with us and saw us at our overwhelming highs and our most sickening lows. To really write this story, a story about a struggling rock band fighting their own demons and the world's perceptions, you have to be able to see the person and not the quasi-rockstar. I don't think many would have made the same kind of observations.

The tour ended on August, 29th, 2006. We came home and went five different ways, and we didn't meet up again as a group until October. When finances came back, the Bowling For Soup tour cost us $19,000. We didn't tour lavishly, there were no five-star hotels, there was no beer budget, and we had $20 per diems (everyone gets twenty dollars for the day to live). I know that's more than some bands get, but I want everyone to be clear about our reality. After playing for almost three months straight in over fifty cities in front of more than 25,000 people, Lucky Boys Confusion incorporated was in the hole for $4,000. That's including the Chicago Beat Kitchen shows and all of the merchandise we sold.

Great memories, no matter how great, don't pay the rent. After working so hard for so long, we had to borrow money for bills when we came home. I don't know where we'd be if it wasn't for our amazing loved ones.

October 2006. Bar Louie. Naperville.

In typical Lucky Boys Confusion-style, we decided to meet at a bar to discuss our future. I was the first one there, as usual. The guys slowly filtered in. Adam and Joe, in typical fashion, came in together and late but not late enough that anyone would want to say anything. We ordered our drinks – 3 Coronas, one rum and Coke, and a water. The meeting went much smoother than anyone had expected.

We decided that we still liked playing music with each other and that there was no reason to stop playing; we just decided to move forward with other aspects of life that we had put on hold because of LBC. We also came to the conclusion that we were done with any major touring. For the first time in ten years, Lucky

Boys Confusion wasn't the most important thing in my life, and to be honest, it was a strange relief. The proverbial wall that the music industry had put up in front of me was crumbling, and I could move on with my life both socially and musically. It was bittersweet, to say the least.

I remember stopping at my parents' house after the meeting. I knew they were in India, but I went anyway. Maybe I just needed to feel something familiar. I sat down in the family room where I had played as a child, now completely devoid of any signs of commotion or horseplay, and turned on the TV. I think the news was on. Without warning I began to laugh hysterically, and as much as I tried to stop, I couldn't, and then for no apparent reason, I started to cry. I finally understood why people act this exact same way when someone close to them dies. After a good half hour, I got up, stretched, and went home to my future wife to start my new life.

A friend of mine from one of the opening bands on the tour sat me down after the rumors about our "meltdown" had reached his ears, and we started talking about the business. This conversation will stick with me forever.

He said, "You know what? I really wish Fall Out Boy and My Chemical Romance the best because I think they're great, and I'm happy they have houses in the hills. But I just want to know, where's my piece of the pie? I don't need a big piece, I just don't understand why the whole pie goes to them."

I just smiled at him and said, "If it didn't, being a rockstar wouldn't be so special."

Stubhy Pandav
4/23/07

Compression

The van was quiet.

Jason drove in silence. Seated next to him in the passenger seat was Stubhy.

Behind Jason was Adam, smoking and staring out the window at passing lights.

There would be no more discussion of music tonight.

Beside Adam, struggling to read in the meager light cast by a small traveler's book lamp, was Joe. He reread the same paragraph three or four times before finally snapping the book shut to gaze out the window at the same passing lights for several minutes before attempting to read the passage again.

In the rear of the van, seated alone with a bench to himself, was Ryan. Some current of anxiety yet coursed beneath the façade of his apparent indifference, electrifying his skin and turning it uncomfortable to the touch. He withdrew his phone, scanned the illuminated phonebook and called a name. A moment later an automated message responded, and Ryan sighed in defeat, too despondent to leave a message.

Something gnawed at his peace.

This road was not long enough.

Equal parts sadism and delirious intoxication called to Ryan as it called to the others in the van with him. It was palpable, like a perfume of cigarettes, whiskey and lipstick. Like the addict called back to his pipe fully aware what horrors lay in wait, they wanted the road. A boyhood vitality still thrummed inside each of their hearts, wanting to play, craning necks out of windows to feel a summer wind upon the cheek as though to affirm that the world, in all of its ephemeral splendor, was still there.

They were languishing. Lucky Boys Confusion had not been home for this long in over two and a half years, and it was becoming difficult to stay their restless tendencies.

There were stories on the road; at home there was only life and its passing trivialities.

Joe had become reckless. Sleeping with coworkers did not offer a suitable enough distraction when he was not yet their superior, and so he had devised little 'happenings' designed to entertain his days behind the counter at a local coffee shop. One morning he told his coworkers and a contingent of groggy patrons that he had put several spoonfuls of his grandmother's ashes into the Arabian Hazelnut.

"She was Swedish. Can you tell?"

When one girl asked him, incredulously, if this were true, he had replied that he was only joking. The powder, he told her, had been nothing more than common household bleach that he had accidentally spilled into the coffee grounds. The girl had nodded a little thickly and said, "So long as it wasn't a dead person."

Jason, employed in a local music shop, had quietly begun tuning the guitars to give strange sounds, toying with octaves and creating hybrids so that, while they didn't sound right, these guitars didn't quite sound out of tune either. Novice players looked at the instruments with a mixture of confused insecurity and tried tweaking the tunings before replacing the guitar upon the rack, looking toward the drums in defeat.

But these were all meaningless distractions.

All around them, both within and without, were reminders of the stage.

There was no more record label, no more Elektra and no more radio rotation. Whispers had begun to call from the shadows as the infuriating ennui crept with tickling feelers over their spirits, molesting unwanted doubts and repressed anxieties.

Rehearsal that night had been another routine reminder.

"So right here," Adam said, "you come in with something like this." Adam played an idea of the sound he wanted while Joe listened and waited.

"Okay," Joe said when Adam had finished, "but my issue is that if I'm going to play that, then this section should be slower. It should build and then sort of bridge."

Adam silently expressed his frustration, saying nothing.

"Adam," Joe repeated, "this part should be slower."

"I'll play it slower when I'm old. It needs to sound fast. We're not playing for geriatrics ... yet."

Later, during a heated debate between Joe and Stubhy, Ryan had sat at his drum kit, twirling his sticks until a moment of inspiration overtook him and he burst out, "Fuck it, guys! Let's get some vodka and women!"

The van exited the expressway and snaked along a desolate suburban road, passing several strip malls and residential housing units still under construction. Ahead lay a crossing over train tracks.

Perhaps the music in the car or the monotony of the drive had distracted him. Perhaps an unconscious suicidal attraction compelled him, or perhaps Jason was merely lost in his own thoughts. Whatever the reason, as Jason approached the crossing, he seemed not to notice the flashing lights or the syncopated alarm bells. Stubhy, slow to perceive the impending disaster as though it couldn't possibly be happening, remained quiet until the last possible moment.

"Dude. Dude, you're—*JASON!*"

Jason awoke from his meditation. Seeing in that instant that he was too close to stop, his speed making it certain that the van would skid into the oncoming train whose lights and horn now flooded the van, he slammed on the accelerator. The van was slow to react, the thundering struggle of the engine giving Jason a moment to regret his decision and offer final amends for all of his past transgressions. Then the van's speed picked up and they were propelled forward, bouncing over the tracks just ahead of the pounding maelstrom of the train.

Safely clear of the tracks, Jason slammed on the brakes and swerved to the side of the road, jerking to a restless stop. His hands gripped the steering wheel, straining his knuckles white.

Stubhy's arms were stiff, one hand gripping the door, the other bracing itself against the dashboard. He said nothing to his friend, and the entire van was still for some moments until, in the rear of the van, Ryan stirred. He turned to look out of the back windows at the gentle, sighing ebb of the passing boxcars. Raising his fist above his head, he shouted, "Hey, you fucking *lunatic*! Watch where the fuck you're going!"

Turning back to the heads of his friends seated in front of him, he added, "That guy's a menace. We ought to report him."

Silence again blanketed the van until Adam began to chuckle. He lit another cigarette.

Joe took a deep breath and, opening his book, said, "Lost my spot."

Jason stayed at the side of the road a few minutes more, and no one chided him or urged him to hurry. No one offered to drive in his stead.

Turning back onto the road some time later, he said only, "I wonder where that train was going."

Cleveland

The crowd waited.

Shoulder to shoulder, longing eyes beseeching the stage, they tensed, quivering with expectation.

The stage lights receded into darkness.

There was movement ahead, and four silhouettes stalked onto the darkened stage. One approached a microphone stand and stood, center stage, silent and immobile. It gripped the microphone as though it meant to drive it into the Earth, a knight before his sword, ready for battle. Two others slung sashes over their necks, and now long staffs protruded from their waists, cutting through the air like wielded lances. The fourth silhouette collapsed forcefully onto a stool behind them, a kamikaze captain adjusting several controls, preparing to fly into the heart of another hurricane.

The lights remained dark, refusing to ignite.

From the sold-out house there arose a cautious salute, the shoulders uncomfortable and impatient.

Still no lights.

Still only four.

The center silhouette's turned head seemed to glare across the stage and into the darkness, jaw clenched, the shadow hands griping the microphone tighter.

A single wooden drumstick struck metal.

The crowd sighed, swelled, and waited.

Darkness.

The lights refused.

A loud shudder breached the tension, a clap of thunder before the execution.

From the rear of the crowded hall a lone figure staggered forward upon licorice legs. It steadied itself, then made a course toward the stage, pushing, nudging, excusing, proceeding. It came forward, ambled left, recovered right, came forward again, darted right.

Abreast of the stage it grunted and hoisted itself up.

This new, fifth silhouette stumbled forward and slung a strap over its shoulder. The shadow's posture, before clumsy and awkward, now became graceful. The shoulders seemed broader, the back straighter, the legs lithe and poised. It lit a cigarette, and a small orange beacon flared and receded in the darkness.

"Ryan," the new arrival said through clenched teeth. "Count it off."

The seated silhouette raised two sticks into the air and struck them together four times. Upon the fifth count the stage erupted into a maelstrom of thrashing confrontation, guitars and cymbal crashes and stage lights bursting to life.

The Lucky Boys Confusion tour had begun, and the crowd, now satisfied, erupted, dancing and singing in one convulsing, effusive mass.

"Get that girl a beer!" someone shouted.

"What?"

"A fucking beer! She's drunk!"

"But—"

"But what?" the voice demanded, impatient.

"Is she crying or laughing?"

This is backstage after a show, and it is always alive. During the daytime hours sunlight invades the grime-gutted recesses and beer-sour crags behind the curtains, making it a lonely and desolate place. But at night, in the security of shadows, this world belongs to revelry.

On this night, as on any other, Adam and Stubhy venture out into the departing crowd, collecting around the merchandise table to greet fans, sign autographs and take pictures. Ryan, Joe and Jason meander through the crowd, drifting from one pocket of eager conversation to the next, smiling and saying a million thank-you's and offering the occasional hug to a shy young fan who can hardly speak and only looks with admiring eyes up toward the flesh and blood face from their imaginations.

For these kids their worries and teenage struggles are forgotten in the moment that they feel the glamour of coming face to face with their icon from the stage.

These are the faces of the adolescent struggle for belonging. They are the nervous and searching expressions of wounded insecurity that find relief in this concert hall world of acceptance and approval. Here they thrive and seem to glimpse some portion of a world removed from their adolescent doubts.

Interspersed among these are the jaded countenances of innocence long lost. These figures wear their skirts a little shorter, their shirts a little tighter, their lipstick a little thicker. These are the faces that left home but never opened the door, the mouths that bit into an apple full of ashes.

These faces, pretty though weathered beyond than their twenty-odd years, show a marked interest in the band members. When they ask, they usually receive backstage access.

And backstage after the fans have left, a second show begins.

"So what I'm looking most forward to about the apocalypse is being able to park in front of fire hydrants," I heard Joe say as he passed, talking with the singer from one of the opening acts. Joe, lead guitar for Lucky Boys Confusion, enjoys literary references and obscure observations. A good conversationalist, his gentle exterior and subtle wit masks the playful, sometimes caustic deviousness watching and waiting just behind his endearing smile.

"I'm just saying that if you have the Olsen twins in the same room together, why not pay them to fight to see which one's the dominant one?" came another voice, talking with a roadie. "You know, most of us consume our twin in the womb and in nature—"

"Dude! You've been on about the Olsen twins all night! Let it *go*!" his friend said as they walked by.

I was standing alone, nursing the first of many beers, watching. I could not deny a certain degree of pride that I should

"The girl whose shoes he puked on."

"Oh," he said, losing interest. "Her name's Angela or something. She's coming out with us. He's going to buy her an apology drink, and I think Joe has a thing for her friend. They're both coming, but they have a chauffeur with them."

"A chauffeur?"

"That's the guy who hangs around the groupie girls and drives them around for us. The chauffeur brings them to the show, the bars, the hotel. They're sort of spineless pushovers who never get to sleep with the girls they fawn over. They're like Tanner, but with less personality."

"Hey!" Tanner shouted, coming up from behind us. "I'm not a fucking chauffeur!"

Adam turned and wrapped an arm around his friend's shoulder. "Of course not, Tanner! You're just unappreciated!"

"Damn right!" he said. "And I locked the keys in the van!"

We left the concert venue after all of the free beer had been drunk, and at our first bar Rosemary began drinking herself into a strange psychosis, chasing whiskey and Sambuca shots with Bud Light and martinis while nearby patrons looked on in disgusted horror.

As Rosemary stood at the bar finishing a cigarette and waiting to order more drinks, a man, middle aged and alone and clinging desperately to the natural color of his hair, finally said something.

"You really shouldn't be drinking like that."

Rosemary glanced in his direction. He was sitting one stool away from where she stood. "I know. 'Beer before liquor, never been sicker,' right? I'm terrible when I start drinking early."

"No, that's not what I—"

"Another round of Sambuca shots and another Bud Light," Rosemary told the bartender.

"You shouldn't be smoking either."

"What?" Rosemary said, half listening as she counted her money with some difficulty.

"How many months along are you?" the man asked.

Rosemary looked up at him with a puzzled expression. Then, remembering the false protrusion just below her chest and its illusion of motherhood, her eyes came alive.

"Seven months, maybe eight. I don't know, how the fuck am I supposed to keep track of these things?"

"That's despicable," the man said, clearly disgusted.

"Well it's not like I *wanted* it," Rosemary said, her voice rising. "This shit just happens."

"Aren't you worried about what you're doing to your child?"

With a force that seemed more than just playful character acting, Rosemary shouted, "Hey! I'm just trying to have a good time!"

Ryan turned around in search of his next shot. The rest of us, Adam, Stubhy, Joe, Angelica, her friend Mercedes, their chauffeur and I turned our attentions in Rosemary's direction.

"That's sad," the man said, shaking his head. "Your generation, you just don't think of anyone but yourself."

"Hey!" Rosemary shouted, now leaning in and poking her finger into the middle of the man's chest. "This is who I *am*! This is what I *do*!"

"You ought to be ashamed of yourself!" the man said, his own voice rising. "You're going to be sorry when your child is born with defects because of your drinking!"

"Yeah," Rosemary said, "but at least it won't be as quarrelsome and defiant as my first two."

The man looked to Ryan.

"Are you the father?"

"The jury's still out," he said.

Rosemary looked a little miffed at this remark.

The bartender poured our shots. He hadn't noticed Rosemary's stomach in the dim lighting, and only her chest had appeared above the edge of the bar. It's possible that he had been too distracted by the breasts shaded beneath the thin fabric of her dress to discern her apparent pregnancy below.

Rosemary downed two of the shots at once. She turned back to the man, cringed, belched and said, "Drinking for two now."

"See?" Ryan said. "That's selfless."

22

"What an absolute disgrace!" the man shouted, breaking his reserve and leaping from his stool. Looking to the bartender, he pointed at Rosemary and said, "You've got to cut this despicable woman off!"

"Hey! Who're you to judge me?" Rosemary said, stumbling backward under the weight of the drink and slurring her words. "You're not my father! And anyway, it might be his!"

Rosemary finished by sweeping the empty shot glasses and one half-empty beer off of the bar. A good portion of the beer sloshed onto the man's shirt and faded khakis as it fell, and that was when the bartender instructed us to leave.

As the rest of us downed the rest of our drinks and turned to go, Stubhy noticed that Angelica, who had been silent, looked a little perturbed.

"What's the matter, Angelina?" he asked. "You look upset."

She turned to him. "It's Angelica."

"What?"

"You called me Angelina. My name's Angelica."

"Oh," Stubhy said. He paused, considering. "Po-tayto pa-tahto."

Mercedes giggled.

Rosemary flicked a cigarette butt across the bar at the bartender's chest.

"All of you! Take your business elsewhere!" the bartender shouted, pointing to the door. "Now!"

At the next bar, her martini cutting through the air in reckless flourishes as her arms flew about her like some spastic marionette, Rosemary said, "I think pop culture is a lot like nazi youth. It's amazing how little persuading it takes to push people into following your lead, chasing the same obsession, the same fish." She drew heavily from her glass, leaving it dry. She hiccupped and said, "Happiness!"

We were standing in the kind of bar that one would expect to find in a lonely corner of hell, populated by aging Abercrombie and Fitch models still chanting 'Chug! Chug!' at two in the morning. The décor appeared to have been salvaged from the recent closings of an Applebee's restaurant and a Pottery Barn, and the lighting was soft enough, in conjunction with the plumes of smoke that hung in the air in a thick yellow smog, to conceal the pock marks and acne scars and thick cakings of Maybelline cosmetics on the women trying to live out their college lifestyle from deep inside of their late thirties.

Following our eviction from the last bar, there was a sense that we were only biding time until Rosemary would create another spectacle, and so we suffered the atmosphere with good humored anticipation.

"That is poetry," Ryan said, smiling and putting an arm around Rosemary.

"I hate poetry," Rosemary said. "Much madness is divinest sense."

"That has to make you divinity's sage," Stubhy said, passing her and stepping up to the bar.

"It takes dedication to be one of the beautiful people," Rosemary said, following a conversation in her mind. "You have to wear a smile like an insignia. I should know—I've modeled."

A woman wearing a look of indignant disgust approached Rosemary from behind. She tapped Rosemary on the shoulder a little petulantly and said, "Excuse me, miss."

The woman was tall. She appeared to be in her late thirties, and her blonde hair had faded, becoming sandy and brittle, falling in a thin curtain about her increasingly gaunt features.

Still facing us, Rosemary's eyes brightened with an intense fire and a slight, fiendish smile lifted one corner of her mouth.

Turning around she said, "In case you've never shopped anywhere outside of a Wal-Mart, that's a Versace you were just touching, so why don't you keep your grubby little finger off of my mother-fucking shoulder."

"Just what in the hell do you think you're doing?" the woman demanded.

"I'm driving a bus, bitch. What the hell does it look like I'm doing? I'm getting wasted!"

"You're pregnant!" the woman screamed, pointing at Rosemary's torso.

"Christ," Rosemary said, rolling her eyes. "Here we go again. What're you, my fucking keeper? Why don't you mind your own fucking business?"

"You're an absolute disgrace!"

Rosemary took a drag from her cigarette, taking care to maintain eye contact with the woman as she did so, choosing her words. "Better a beautiful disgrace than ugly and chaste." Exhaling into the woman's face and flicking the butt to the floor, she added, "Your virtue wasn't a choice."

"You're vile," the woman said in a hoarse whisper, full of venom. "And you're a despicable mother."

"Me?" said Rosemary, raising her eyebrows and pointing a finger at herself in feigned disbelief. "Do you have any kids? Or are you afraid your desiccated vaginal tract is already barren? Maybe you'll never get to know the simple pleasures of caesarian scars and child abuse."

The woman's mouth dropped open, and she gaped at Rosemary in renewed shock.

Rosemary lit another cigarette and continued. "Most kids grow up to hate their parents anyway. Better to give them a good reason, I say. And we should tell our daughters that it's because we love them when we beat them. The world needs strippers."

"I'm not too old to have kids," the woman said, her voice faltering. "I'm only thirty-n—"

"Fuck me," Rosemary continued. "Mine is the beating of an infernal heart. Yours is the ticking of an infernal clock."

The woman took a step forward, fangs barred, dripping with vitriol. She raised her hand to strike Rosemary.

Rosemary took no retreating step backward. She merely leaned back, raised her left hand, palm outward, and pointed to her stomach with her right. "Ah-ah-ah. How would you look trying to defend yourself in court after striking a pregnant woman?"

The woman froze, her eyes shimmering with the soft wetness of incipient tears.

Her friends, who had watched the scene unfold, were conspicuously silent as they reserved their own criticisms for Rosemary's turned back.

"If you want, you can have this one," Rosemary finished. "I have a feeling it's going to be defective anyway. I'll give you a heck of a deal for it."

The woman lowered her hand and stared through another cloud of smoke from Rosemary's cigarette. With a quick but forceful gesture she dipped her head and spat at Rosemary's feet, just missing her shoe. Having made her point she turned back to her friends.

Rosemary watched her go and called after her, "See? Spitting. You'll never get pregnant that way!"

It wasn't until Rosemary threw her drink into another woman's face and Stubhy began "Thunder Pumping" the juke box that we were finally evicted. I was in the bathroom during this spectacle, and when I came out everyone had already made it halfway down the block to the next bar.

"What is thunder pumping?" I asked again when I caught up with them. But no one seemed interested in answering me.

At the next bar Rosemary made a bee line for the bathroom. Standing at the bar waiting to order drinks, Ryan took notice of an older man seated near him. The man appeared sullen and unoccupied, his arms folded before him on the bar, and Ryan thought he might attempt to entertain him.

Ryan hailed the bartender and ordered a round of celebratory drinks in a voice that was loud enough for the man to hear. The man eyed Ryan a moment and seemed to decide that he would make good company. "What're you celebrating?" he asked.

"I'm about to be a father," Ryan said, turning his head.

"No fooling! Congratulations! Here, let me buy you a drink."

"Thanks," Ryan said, smiling. "Black Sambuca. And one for yourself."

The man hailed the bartender, amended Ryan's order and laid a twenty on the bar.

"So do you know what it's going to be?" the man asked.

"Sure I do. A pain in the ass!"

The man laughed. "I mean is it going to be a boy or a girl? Or are you waiting to find out?"

"Oh, we're waiting," Ryan said. "It's going to be a surprise."

"I remember my first. My wife and I had an awful argument over the names, we did."

"Oh yeah?"

"Yessir. Let me be the first to tell you, son. Let the little lady have her way in that matter. It'll be better for the both of you, it will."

"I don't believe in letting women have their way all the time," Ryan said. "They lose respect for you."

"Oh, yeah?" the man said, looking speculatively at Ryan. "Well how far along is she?"

"Pretty far, my man. Something like eight months."

"Oh-oh. That's when it's the toughest, isn't it, my friend?" the man said, empathizing. "The emotions start to run wild and it's difficult to move about. My wife had a hard time leaving the house at all, really."

"What? No, she's doing alright. She's right over there," Ryan said, nodding behind the man as Rosemary approached.

The man didn't turn to look but eyed Ryan closely, irritated by what seemed to be his little barroom prank.

When Rosemary appeared at Ryan's side she tripped and wrapped her arms around him to catch herself. Speaking in a stream of almost total incoherence, she said, "Oh hey baby I just spilled my drink allllll down the front of Stubhy's shirt is he mad I told you—I told him you'd buy him another one a drink not a shirt but that's a really nice shirt so maybe he wants you to did you order yet because I need another shot."

The man looked at Rosemary with a mixture of dawning horror and incredulity, gazing stupidly from her stomach to her face to Ryan's smile to the cigarette burning in Rosemary's hand. Rosemary giggled and kissed Ryan's cheek. The bartender placed the two shots intended for Ryan and his new friend down on the bar, and without hesitating, Rosemary took one, drank, slammed the glass down upon the counter and chased it with the second, finishing this with a long draw from her cigarette.

Rosemary turned from the bar and noticed the look on the stranger's face. "Whatz your problem?"

"You're—you're a—a monster!" the man stuttered.

With a dismissive flick of her hand Rosemary said, "Whatever. Thahtz just your opinion."

"You're despicable!" the man shouted. "You're a vile, wretched woman! How dare you—"

"Well, to fuck me is to know me," she said, ashing her cigarette into the man's drink. "Keep that up and I just might go home with *you.*"

"And you're the father?" the man asked, looking to Ryan. "What kind of a man are you to allow this?"

"Hey, don't turn this on me," Ryan said. "She can make her own decisions. You said so yourself."

"But the child!" the man shouted. "You two can't raise a child!"

"Thank God you agree," Ryan said. "I'm hoping I won't have to. I want to keep all of this a secret. Anyway, it's better that her husband doesn't find out it's mine."

"Her *husband!*"

"Don't worry," Rosemary said, still teetering. "He knows it isn't his."

"But he doesn't know it's mine!" Ryan added.

Rosemary then produced a stick of red lipstick from her purse. Giggling, she looked down at her chest and drew a large A upon it, scrawling the red lines across her skin and the fabric of her dress.

When she had finished she spread her arms and looked down at her work. To her, the A was a simple masterpiece in comic irony. To any other observer, however, the insignia looked like an awkward V with a diagonal line drawn haphazardly across it.

Stubhy returned from the bathroom as she finished, and he looked at Rosemary and asked, "What the fuck happened?"

"A study in scarlet. Now I can wear my shame between my legs *and* on my tits!" Rosemary said, collapsing into Ryan's arms in a fit of laughter.

"I get it," Adam said, turning from the bar. "She's a feminist."

Adam then suggested doing body shots off of Rosemary's stomach, and when she climbed onto the bar to oblige him we were evicted and "banned for life."

This was not the last time these words would be used with reference to us this night.

Though he had accompanied us since leaving the concert venue, no one had really noticed Angelica and Mercedes's chauffeur. It wasn't until we had arrived at the hotel that anyone learned his name.

"Daniel," he said, shaking hands with Adam for the second time.

"Let's get a room!" Mercedes said, approaching Daniel with an unsteady gait.

Joe had suggested this earlier.

Daniel was meek without being entirely spineless. He wore modern thick framed glasses, a black t-shirt and new blue jeans, and his hairstyle was trendy and unremarkable. Chauffeurs typically catered to whatever the girls in their service wanted without question, but Daniel seemed to have at least a nascent assertiveness.

"Umm," Daniel said.

"C'mon!" Mercedes pleaded. "This way we won't have to drive home tonight. We can just crash in the room!"

"Do we have enough money?" he asked.

"I do," Mercedes said. "Angelica?"

"Sure. I mean, I guess."

"See? C'mon, it'll be *fun!* We can party all night with Lucky Boys Confusion. How cool is that?" she said, grabbing his arm and cupping his hand into hers.

"Yeah, okay," he said.

Mercedes tossed Daniel's hand away and raised her arms above her head in victory, shouting with joy. She fell onto Joe and added, turning her head back to Daniel, "But you have to register the room in your name because we're too drunk."

Daniel went inside to attend to the room, and Adam telephoned Jason to locate the Lucky Boys rooms. When Jason answered Adam's call, he insisted on calling him King Leo.

29

"Dude, what the fuck is wrong with you?"

"Drunk, King Leo. Quite rather drunk. Your obedient servant the Duke of Tanner is here. He'll be your eunuch. He's already liquored up and pliable to suggestion."

Adam was not amused until Jason managed to explain that there had been a reservation error through the website, and the Crowne Plaza had failed to reserve their rooms. Compounding the problem, the hotel was almost entirely booked. This had appeared an impending disaster until the desk attendant had suggested amending the error by placing them on the top floor and making one of their rooms the Presidential Suite for the price of a regular room.

Daniel and the girls were able to procure a room only because one, a single double bed, had become available through a late cancellation. It was the last remaining vacancy, Daniel was told.

"This room has a fucking conference table in it, King Leo," Jason said. "Tanner's break-dancing on it as we speak."

While everyone went directly to the Presidential Suite, save for Ryan and Rosemary, who retired to Ryan and Joe's room down the hall, I went to my own room. I had checked in earlier that day but had only had time to drop off my luggage before going straight to the concert venue to catch Lucky Boys Confusion's performance. I had not bathed since my daylong trip and this, combined with the heat and congestion of the crowded concert venue, made my presence unpleasant to at least two of five senses.

Personal hygiene aside, my mind was rattled from the sensory overload of returning to the Lucky Boys Confusion liquor train, and so the idea of a few moments' peace possessed a certain appeal. I had come out on tour as part of my own vacation, intending to capture the experience for a book, but I needed a momentary reprieve before recommitting myself to this monster's clutches.

There were long weeks and longer nights ahead.

When I was finished, I took the elevator to the top floor of the hotel. I could feel the pressure change as a soft chime above me marked my ascent. Adam had told me that it would be easy to find their room because it would have a placard beside the door denoting it as the Presidential Suite. I suspected it would be easy to find for other reasons, and in this I was not disappointed.

As I exited the elevator car, a door opened to my left. I heard a voice distinctly Ryan's shout, "She bled all over the bed! She bled all over the bed!"

It was impossible to tell if he was proud or concerned, and recalling Rosemary's fashion accessory from earlier, I thought that this might betoken sad visions of Frieda Kahlo in Detroit at the Henry Ford Hospital. But this vision failed to take into account the fact that Ryan was naked save for a pair of mismatched socks and a bandana tied Rambo-style about his forehead.

He passed me and disappeared into another room farther down the hall. When I was a short distance away from the room into which he had gone, Ryan reappeared, holding aloft a bottle. He looked at me and shouted, "Derek!" before proceeding to his room at the other end of the hall, capering like a bow-legged sprite across flaming hot coals.

Standing just outside the door that had nearly shut behind Ryan, I heard rock n' roll music coming from a small stereo, and behind this there were shouts and cheers and some laughter. Then I heard Stubhy shout, "Thunder Pumping time! It's Thunder Pumping time!"

"No, Stubhy! Don't do it!"

"It's time! No stopping it! She wants it!"

Laughter.

Again Adam said, "Don't do it, don't do it! She's not ready! She needs a gentle lover! You're too rough!"

There was a loud chorus of shouts, and I pushed open the door to see the small crowd turned toward Stubhy as he stood before the television, his pants about his ankles and his cartoon-pirate festooned boxer shorts covering his shame. He had raised one leg in the air and was pressing it against the television, thrusting his hips against the screen while one hand periodically slapped the television's plastic casing.

This, I thought, was the equivalent of a Mexican donkey show, and Adam, Joe, the two girls, Jason, Toadie and Tanner

31

raised cheers as Stubhy mimicked climax, slowed, and then pushed the television from its perch, sending it crashing to the floor.

The crowd gave a final climactic cheer as Stubhy staggered backward from his conquest.

"Derek!" Jason shouted, noticing me. "You just missed Stubhy's latest Thunder Pumping show!"

"I saw it," I said, grabbing the nearest beer and opening it. "I wish I'd seen the one at the bar."

Stubhy pulled up his pants and lit a cigarette.

"I deflowered that bitch at the bar for her own good. If it hadn't been me, it would have been some balding forty-year-old with a thyroid condition and a Bob Seger t-shirt. I performed a service."

The room was impressive, far larger than any of my first college apartments. It was supplied with a kitchen, a living area and a large oak conference table. I wondered if anyone had ever used this table to roll a joint in the same way that Toadie was presently occupied. I had to believe that it probably had, but those people probably hadn't sported several facial piercings and been laden with enough wallet chains to make Jacob Marley's ghost appear a saint by comparison.

At the far end of the room was a large ornamental bookshelf housing an assortment of hardcover books. Some were by popular fiction writers like Stephen King and Tom Clancy, some business books and a few scattered classics thrown in for good measure. Adam stood before these, seemingly perusing their titles with the interest of selecting one for his summertime reading.

Tanner was in rare form, and at odd intervals one would hear him, over the din of music and various pockets of conversation, break into song, raising his fist and rocking his head to his own rhythm. In one particular fit of passion he ascended the conference table where Toadie was still in intense deliberations with a bag of pot and several rolling papers and began shouting the chorus to another song, swaying and holding his beer above his head.

Angelica, Mercedes and Joe stood nearby, and they all turned to look up at him. Toadie shouted irritably at Tanner, trying to shield his pot from Tanner's uncontrolled step, and that was when Adam threw a book at Tanner that crashed into the wall behind Mercedes, who shrieked and covered her head. Adam then threw a second book, a copy of Stephen King's *Carrie*, and this caught Tanner's raised arm and knocked it backward, dousing Angelica with the rest of Tanner's tepid beer.

Angelica's hair, a sandy blond that a moment before had been buoyant with small curls and hairsprayed firmness, now clung to her face, wet, dripping and sticky. Tanner began apologizing to her with genuine sincerity, and when Tanner tried to implicate Adam as partially culpable for the mishap, Adam grabbed another book and made ready to throw it at Tanner. Stubhy, standing near enough, put out his hand and gently lowered Adam's raised arm.

"I'm fucking *soaked!*" Angelica cried, holding out her arms and looking down at herself.

"Hey, do you think we can lift the couch onto the conference table?" Jason asked, rounding the corner from the bedroom. He had missed the start of the small drama presently unfolding. "It would be kind of fun to sit up there, wouldn't it? Sort of regal. Right, King Leo?"

"What's with this King Leo shit?" Adam asked, turning his attention from the Tanner situation.

When Daniel returned a few minutes later from a cigarette run, he fished the room key from his pocket and handed it to Angelica, who wanted to clean herself of Tanner's beer. Meanwhile Adam went to the table and distributed the cigarettes packs to Toadie, Tanner, Joe and himself.

As Daniel was offering to show Angelica and Mercedes to their room, Adam asked him if there was a vending machine on their floor.

"Yeah," Daniel said. "I think so."

"You mind getting me a Coke?"

"Um," Daniel said, recalling the cigarettes he'd just purchased. "You want a Coke?"

"Oh yeah, can I get one, too?" Toadie asked, reaching a hand into his pocket.

"I guess so," Daniel said. "Okay."

"As long as you're going, can I get a Sprite or a Mountain Dew or something?" Stubhy asked, handing Daniel a dollar after Toadie.

"Yeah, okay," Daniel said, trying to sound amenable.

"I'll take a Dr. Pepper," Joe said, giving him another dollar.

"Get me the same," Jason said. "We need something to mix with this rum."

"They've probably got Diet Coke, don't they? Get me one," Tanner said, grabbing an extra dollar from Toadie's hand and giving it to Daniel.

"I think they're a dollar fifty," Daniel started to say.

"And get an extra something for Ryan," Jason said, giving him still another dollar. "Maybe a Sprite or something."

"Wait, let me see. That's a Diet, a Dr. Pepper, a Mountain Dew, another Dr. Pepper," Daniel said.

"Or its equivalent," Jason added. "Mr. Pibb or whatever."

"A Coke," Daniel continued.

"No substitutions," Adam said. "Only Coke."

"I think it's a Pepsi machine," Daniel said, looking at Adam.

"What? Are you sure? Well, fuck it then, give me back my dollar." Adam reached out and took one of the dollars from Daniel's hand. Daniel didn't seem to want to tell Adam that he hadn't given him a dollar in the first place.

"What's the difference?" he asked instead.

"What's the difference?" Adam asked. "You use Pepsi for enema bags and industrial-strength douches, not for drinking. You're better off mixing a cocktail with Drano."

"You are what you eat," Joe said to Daniel, "and what you drink. That's why you don't see us drinking Zima or Snapple. It says that we stand up to pee."

"I like Zima," Tanner said.

"So if they don't have Dr. Pepper, you don't want anything?"

"Oh, no. I don't care," Joe said. "I don't discriminate."

Daniel left without further clarification and caught up with Angelica and Mercedes near the elevators. While they waited, Ryan emerged again from his room, backing out of it

34

slowly as if backing away from an armed assassin. To Daniel and the girls there seemed to be some commotion coming from inside that receded as the door clicked softly shut.

Ryan turned and saw the three of them.

"Hey!" he shouted, his apprehension flying from him. He approached them, jovial and clothed, and stopped. "Jesus, Allison. What the fuck happened to you?"

There was a tense pause.

"Look at you," he continued, looking at her figure. "You're absolutely soaked."

"It's not Allison," she said, glaring up at him.

"What?"

"It's *Angelica*."

"Oh," Ryan said. Then, shrugging, he added, "To-mayto ta-mahto."

A soft chime sounded, and Daniel and the two girls went silently inside the waiting elevator car before Angelica could make things more uncomfortable. As the doors closed, Ryan shouted, "Hey! Wait!" but it was too late.

"Shit," he said. "I could've asked them to get me a Coke."

After Daniel and the girls left, Joe discovered Ryan's backpack. Jason had accidentally brought this to the Presidential Suite while unloading the van earlier, and this would prove a significant oversight considering later events.

"What room did they say they were in?" Joe asked, rummaging through its contents.

"Five thirteen," Jason said. "Why?"

Joe didn't answer. He smiled as he found what he was looking for.

Ryan pounded on the door of the Presidential Suite.

"Open this fucking door! Pack your bags! You don't belong here!"

This sudden outburst from the hallway startled Toadie, who had been reposing on the couch beside Jason, smoking. Their feet hung over the edge of the couch, some four feet from the ground. It hadn't required much effort to lift the couch onto the large conference table, as Jason had suggested. With four of us hoisting it the task had been easy, though we had nearly crushed Tanner's hand when he placed it on the edge of the table for balance while adjusting his shoe, seemingly oblivious to what we were doing.

Toadie now wore a shower cap, a peculiar habit of his whenever he smoked pot in hotels on tour. Adam and Tanner sat in chairs, scanning through Jason's music files on his laptop and arguing over song selections. Joe and Stubhy had left shortly before with mischief in their eyes.

I opened the door for Ryan, who entered and demanded to know where Joe and Stubhy had gone.

"They left without saying. My guess is that they went to Andrea and Mercedes's room looking for some action," Adam said.

"I just saw those chicks a minute ago," Ryan said.

"Amber almost spilled our pot," Toadie said. "That chick's a pain in the ass."

"They didn't say much, but what the fuck happened to her?" Ryan asked. "She looked pissed."

"Tanner happened to her," Toadie said.

"*Adam* is the one who threw the book! He started it!" Tanner said, jumping to his feet and flying into another dramatic defense.

"Shut up, Tanner," Adam said without looking up. "Your excuses only make you look guilty." Then, turning to Ryan, he asked, "So what's up with Rosemary?"

Ryan grimaced. "Suffice to say, she's not exactly marriage material."

"You might have thought of that before you knocked her up," Adam said, turning his attention back to the music.

"Wait, you got some girl pregnant?" Tanner asked.

"Shut up, Tanner," Toadie called from the couch.

Ryan uncapped the bottle of rum. "We got anything to mix this with?"

"It's coming," Jason said from the couch.

Ryan shrugged, put the bottle to his lips and drew deeply.

A moment later there was another knocking at the door, and when Ryan went to open it, he saw Daniel juggling a multitude of soda bottles, clearly agitated and excited. He entered and spilled the bottles onto the counter.

Turning to Ryan, he said, "Umm. You know about Rosemary?"

"She shaves it. So?"

"She's downstairs in the lobby," Daniel said.

"Can you toss me the Pepsi?" Toadie called from the couch.

"Hey, toss me that Dr. Pepper," Jason said.

"Cool," Tanner said. "You got my Diet!"

"I'm drinking Stubhy's Mountain Dew," Adam said to himself.

"Rosemary, she's downstairs in the lobby," Daniel said.

"I don't think you want to mix rum with Mountain Dew, King Leo."

"It'll work," Adam said. "Beggars, you know, cannot be, uh …"

"For that matter, I'm not so sure that you want to mix it with Diet either, Tanner," Jason added.

"I don't give a fuck!"

"She's making quite a scene," Daniel said.

"It mixes great with regular Pepsi, though," Toadie said. "Pass the bottle up here when you're finished."

"Hey, cool, you got me a Dr. Pepper, too!" Ryan said.

"That's actually for," Daniel began, then changed his mind. "I mean, Rosemary is acting really crazy," he tried again.

"There's a newsflash," Ryan said, pouring rum into a cup.

"Are you guys done? Pass the bottle up here!" Toadie demanded.

"Hey, this doesn't taste too bad," Tanner said, sipping his cocktail.

"She's like, screaming and stuff," Daniel said.

"I bet it'd taste better with a little lime juice," Jason said.

"You have no taste," Toadie said. "Let me see the bottle."

"Didn't Joe get something, too?" I asked.

"You have to be here to get it," Adam said. "They'll have to get their own."

"She's acting really crazy, is all. She's screaming and stuff. In the lobby."

"He's going to be pissed. Where the fuck is he?" Ryan asked.

"Sorry, dude. I spilled some of yours," Tanner said.

"No problem, just hurry up with the rum and pass it up here," Toadie said.

"I mean, she's acting *really* crazy, you know. Rosemary is."

Ryan turned to Daniel. "We *heard* you, my man. Don't worry. Relax and have a drink."

Daniel fell silent. By the time he had collected his thoughts, most of the soda bottles were opened and sitting about the counter half full. He scrambled to find a cup and pour himself some Pepsi and then waited for the rum.

"Rum's gone," Toadie said, throwing the empty bottle across the room where it landed with a hollow thud.

Daniel tried to hide is disappointment.

"So, when did you realize that Rosemary was nuts?" I asked, turning to Ryan.

"Well," Ryan began, swirling his drink as he considered this question. "She wanted to listen to ABBA with the lights on while we had sex. And after we were done she did start punching me in the chest, screaming 'You fucked me, you fucked me you son of a bitch, who do you think you are?' That was sort of odd, I guess."

"But not for you," Adam said.

Ryan smiled. "But she was laughing and crying at the same time."

"Then what happened?" I asked.

"Then I ran down the hall to where you guys were and got the bottle of Smirnoff. I thought if anything deserved a toast, that sure did."

"You were screaming something about her bleeding all over the bed, too," I said.

"Oh, yeah. She did. It might have been strawberry daiquiri, though. I'm not sure."

"Umm," Daniel said, raising his hand. We looked at him, inviting him to speak. "She *is* downstairs right now, in the lobby, screaming about how the father of her child doesn't know who the mother is."

We nodded indifferently. The importance of this fact paled in comparison to the story of Ryan's recent conquest.

"So," Daniel continued, "I mean, maybe we should—"

"Oh! That reminds me," Ryan said, turning back to us. "She wanted to have sex with that pregnancy stomach thing on. She wore it underneath that baby-doll dress. I mean, who still wears those baby-doll dresses? I thought those were like a 90's thing."

"She's stuck in the past," Jason agreed.

"It was sort of hard to maneuver around at first, but I kind of liked it. It was like a pillow you could rest on every now and then."

"If it was real you might've felt it kicking," I said.

"That's sick, dude," Adam said, lighting a cigarette.

"Hey, David," Ryan said, turning to Daniel. "Where'd you get those smokes?"

"Wait a minute," Adam interjected, turning to Daniel as well. "Why were you in the lobby anyway?"

"I couldn't find any vending machines that worked so I went to the first floor where I had seen some others when I checked in. That's when I saw Rosemary. I don't think she saw me, though. I was kind of trying to avoid her."

"Like a seasoned pro!" Ryan exclaimed. "That's exactly what you do in that situation—deny association. Good work."

"Oh. Uh, thanks."

"He's right," Adam said. "At that point the situation's out of your hands."

"It's not about you, so don't try to be a hero," Jason said.

"Spoken like a gentleman," Adam said, raising his glass. We toasted Daniel's competence.

There was a rattling at the door and Stubhy and Joe returned. They entered with strange grins, and they appeared about to speak when they noticed Daniel. They looked back to each other in silent conference, and said nothing.

Joe approached the counter and mixed together the remainder of the sodas into two glasses, and Stubby produced a small flask of vodka from his pocket which he shared with Joe.

They clinked glasses and sat in the two chairs near the fallen TV, still smiling.

"What the fuck is going on with you two?" Ryan asked.

"Nothing," Stubhy said.

"Nope," Joe added.

"All's well."

"Couldn't be better."

They sat upright in their chairs, stiff, a fire dancing in their eyes.

"Is it something to do with Rosemary?" Jason asked. "We've just heard about her."

"Rosemary?" Joe asked.

"Never heard of her." Stubhy said.

"Is she one of yours?"

"Is she one of mine?"

Daniel's phone rang. "Hello?" he said, answering.

"Then why do you two look so suspicious?" Jason continued.

"Who?" Joe asked.

"Us?" Stubhy said.

"Do we?"

"No reason."

"What's with all the questions?"

"Who's on trial?"

Daniel became flustered and began to talk rapidly into his phone. "What? I—wait a minute," he stammered. "Why? What did they do?"

Stubhy and Joe's eyes remained fixed on Jason, consciously ignoring Daniel's conversation while Jason and the rest of us turned to Daniel, who became increasingly panicked.

"Right now? But—how much? With *what*?" He looked at Stubhy and Joe, who now turned to look at him. Daniel saw two people he admired and slightly feared. He could not yell at them when he so desperately wanted their acceptance.

"Okay, okay," he said. "I'll be right down."

Daniel snapped his phone shut and rose to leave.

"What's going on, dude?" Tanner asked.

"I—we're getting kicked out."

"Shit. What'd those chicks do?" Tanner asked.

40

"They didn't," he began, and looked at Joe and Stubhy. "I have to go," he said, heading toward the door.

"Tell Alicia I'm sorry," Tanner called after him. The door shut on Tanner's last words. "Shit. I hope it wasn't because of me."

"It's not always about you, Tanner," Adam said.

"I didn't *say* that!"

"Shut up, Tanner," Toadie said.

The next day we were able to piece together what happened following Daniel's departure using fragments of accounts from Joe, Stubhy and a female housekeeper whom Stubhy befriended early the next morning.

"You have to understand that we had only good intentions," Joe told us. "We didn't know the windows wouldn't open and that the smoke would drift into the hallway. And anyway, the smoke alarms didn't go off or anything, so it could've been worse."

He was referring to the fact that when Stubhy and Joe left the Presidential Suite shortly after Daniel and the girls, they had gone to room 513 armed with the fireworks that Joe had found in Ryan's backpack. Mercedes had admitted them to the room, and they went directly into the bathroom where they began to light long strings of the fireworks in the bathtub. The unexpected explosions had distressed Angelica enough to send her screaming from the bathroom in the midst of washing her face and her hair, though her screams could hardly be heard over the sonorous echo of the explosions reverberating off of the porcelain and tile.

Mercedes, fully aware that there would be no dissuading Joe and Stubhy or appealing to their sense of reason, had gone to the window and attempted to open it. She struggled with this for a short time while Angelica continued screaming and shouting at Joe and Stubhy to stop. This perhaps only incited them further as they turned from the fireworks in the bathtub to the unopened packages of bottle rockets which they began lighting in their hands, playfully shooting them at each other as they chased each other around the room.

At this point Mercedes's calm reserve failed, and she too began screaming and running about the room in a growing fit of hysteria, covering her head and seeking shelter. Angelica found herself cowering beneath the bed, no longer screaming but shielding her ears from the explosions about her.

"Chicks have pillow fights and guys have bottle rocket fights. It's just nature," Joe said. "I didn't think we were doing anything wrong. I thought the girls were having fun."

One bottle rocket flew through Mercedes's hair and exploded just beyond her head as she ran screaming toward the bathroom. The shock caused her to stumble, and the fingernails of her right hand tore into the canvas of a cheap painting of a pastel summertime cottage as she fell. A dusting of paint and canvass sprinkled down upon her like holiday confetti.

After the last rocket exploded a short time later, the room resembled a Scottish moor thick with fog, the light struggling through the haze of spent gun powder. Joe and Stubhy were doubled over with laughter, and the only sound that escaped their exhausted lungs was a hoarse, choked gasp.

Apart from this, the room was silent.

Angelica had cautiously peered out from under the bed, ready to duck back underneath if another rocket should fly from out of another hand. Mercedes began to cough, looking bewilderedly about her, trying to comprehend what had happened.

The momentary quiescence was broken moments later by the ringing of the room telephone. Mercedes looked horror-stricken in its direction.

"I thought that might be the front desk. I was pretty sure that we had woken up some people in the other rooms," Joe told us. "That was about the time that Stubhy and I decided to leave."

"I don't think they understood what would happen if they stayed in the room and tried to reason with hotel management," Stubhy said. "But there was no point in trying to explain it to them. They weren't in a mood to listen. I told Andrea not to answer the phone and Mercedes to try opening the window to air the smoke out of the room. Then we left."

Several minutes after Joe and Stubhy had disappeared into their own elevator car, hotel security pounded on the door

42

to room 513. When Angelica answered, her mascara running down her face with the tears, sweat and beer of that evening, Mercedes was visible behind her as she stood on the edge of the bed using a pillow case to try to fan the smoke away from the smoke detector that had erupted in intermittent bursts of warning.

The security guard was already irritable from having to speak with a pregnant woman who appeared to be incredibly drunk. This girl, whom Richard had begun to refer to as 'The V-Girl' because of the strange V smeared in lipstick across her chest, had demanded that she be given a room, saying that she could pay for it when she found her baby's father the next morning.

She had said all of this while screaming in Richard's face and poking her finger into the middle of his chest.

When he had told her, sternly, that she would have to leave and that she would no longer be welcomed in any Crowne Plaza hotels in the future, she had screamed back at him, "Fuck you! I don't even have a room here! First you tell me that there aren't any rooms and now you're telling me that me and my unborn child can never come back? You chauvinist fucking pig! You don't know what it's like to be a woman and have to carry the world's sins inside of your pussy!"

He had had to leave her downstairs after several customers reported loud explosions and smoke coming from somewhere on the fifth floor, and so when he saw the inside of room 513, he quickly decided to escort the two young girls downstairs and evict them along with the other woman.

Back downstairs he must have been a little surprised to see that all three girls apparently knew each other. He couldn't have known how their stories intertwined, and he probably didn't care, either. One can imagine that he wanted them sent away as soon as possible and that he was certain he didn't get paid enough to deal with this kind of shit.

Things went smoothly enough as he took down the information of the two new girls from room 513. One of the girls had called the guy in whose name the room was rented, and once he got this man's information he would be able to send them all packing.

He was standing at the concierge desk and completing the necessary paperwork when everything went horribly wrong.

"Here's your identification, Mercedes," he said without looking up, handing Mercedes her driver's license. "And here's yours, Angela."

He continued scribbling information on triplicate forms, his hand outstretched, his head still down.

"That's not my name."

Richard continued to hold out her driver's license, still writing.

"Here's your identification," he repeated, seeming not to have heard her.

"It's *Angelica*."

He looked up, frustrated and tired. "What?"

Angelica's eyes were wide. "You just called me Angela. My name's *Angelica*."

He sighed. "Look, po-tayto pa-tahto, sweetheart, just take your goddamned ID and—"

"It's my fucking *name*, you *asshole!*" Angelica screamed.

This is when Angelica began screaming a litany of obscenities and insults at the man, who, taken aback, could only watch with a dumb expression of tired and confused disbelief.

At the sound of Angelica taking up arms to fight the good fight, Rosemary had jumped up from her seat with a little more agility than usual for a woman in her third trimester of pregnancy and joined Angelica, periodically grabbing the sides of her overgrown stomach to punctuate her argument.

Daniel had arrived to the lobby to hear something like, "think you can just fuck whoever you want and there'll be no repercussions for you because you don't have to carry a baby to term and you always get off anyway and do you think that the clitoris is just some urban fucking myth? Some lie designed to make you look incompetent? And do you really think that dragging your dry and canker-sored tongue across it like a piece of sandpaper is supposed to get us off? That's if you have the cojones to venture down there in the first place. Or do you think that if you work it like you're playing a scratch n' win lottery ticket you'll win an orgasm? And then you blame us for that, too, like it's our fault if we require a little finesse and sophistication! Then tell us that we're difficult or that we should've been on the pill or that we shouldn't have let you fuck us in the first place when we should know our cycles and ..."

Angelica, at almost the same pitch and fevered intensity, had shouted something like "look at you like you're something special? How about that, you fucking prick! Think that people don't forget who *you* are, mister big-time? You think that everyone exists only with respect to you? Who the fuck are you? Big-time mister misogynist with a pinky-finger prick looking for another hole to stick it into because the last one walked away disappointed and laughing and ..."

In the end the police had arrived, and along with a lifetime banning, Rosemary and Angelica were cited for disorderly conduct and public drunkenness when they continued to berate hotel security while in the presence of the attending police officers.

Daniel later drove Mercedes and Angelica home while Rosemary was detained further by the police for lecturing and subsequently taken to a nearby hospital where she was instructed to seek immediate medical attention in the interest of her unborn child.

Rosemary had entered the emergency room, waited for the police to leave and then told an inquisitive nurse that her child was going to achieve great things someday.

"He might even be president," she said. "Just you wait."

Then, patting her pockets, she had asked, "You got a smoke I could bum?"

On the Road

Travel log from an average day.

6:00 am

Wake-up call Adam and Joe's room. Joe answers, shouts something unintelligible and hangs up.

6:32 am

Loud knocking on door of room 505. Joe answers. Jason and Stubhy are waiting. They look irritated.

6:45 am

Jason checks out at the front desk. The desk clerk looks irritated.

6:50 am

Lucky Boys Confusion's van, affectionately called 'The Lucky Van,' is on the road.

7:03 am

The Lucky Van stops at a Conoco. Jason buys coffee. Stubhy buys cigarettes and hair dye for "African hair types" from the Walgreens next door. Ryan uses the bathroom. Joe snaps pennies at Tanner.

7:10 am

The Lucky Van is back on the road.

7:15 am

Tanner is asleep; Joe uses a Sharpie to write obscenities on his forehead.

7:23 am

The Lucky Van veers sharply to the shoulder and skids to a stop on loose gravel.

7:24 am

All doors of The Lucky Van simultaneously open and its occupants spill out onto the embankment, scrambling to flee the scene inside. Ryan is last, and he hobbles into nearby bushes.

7:32 am

After airing out the van with cigarettes and matches, all occupants begrudgingly shuffle back into the van. Tanner despondently sits in the seat formerly occupied by Ryan.

7:45 am

Adam requests to stop for cigarettes.

7:48 am

Adam mentions that he is out of cigarettes.

7:51 am

Adam reminds the van that he is out of cigarettes.

7: 53 am

Adam informs the van that he needs cigarettes in the morning.

7:54 am

Adam points out that they are approaching gas stations that sell cigarettes.

8:05 am

The Lucky Van is back on the road.

8:07 am

Joe entertains the van with stories from the previous night involving groupies, glow sticks, whiskey and vibrating cell phones.

8:13 am

Ryan entertains the van with stories from the previous night involving groupies, whiskey, hotel elevators and empty bottles of vodka.

8:22 am

Stubhy tells the van about two girls who had tried to make out with him, lamenting the fact that they weren't just ugly, but "fugly." He is morose because of it.

8:30 am

Toadie complains that Tanner spoiled his attempt to sleep with one girl when he insulted her by saying that she looked like a man. Tanner suggests that Toadie may be gay.

8:35 am

Tanner mentions that he is out of cigarettes.

11:13 am

The Lucky Van stops for lunch at a truck stop diner.

11:15 am

Tanner is refused entry, cited for indecency due to the obscenities written on his face.

11:51 am

LBC and crew leave abruptly after Joe regurgitates his lunch onto his plate.

11:52 am

The Lucky Van is back on the road. Joe curls up on the back bench with a t-shirt wrapped around his eyes.

12:08 pm

Ryan requests to stop to use the bathroom.

12:09 pm

The Lucky Van stops at a gas station.

12:25 pm

Ryan returns to the van refreshed.

12:27 pm

The Lucky Van is back on the road.

12:30 pm

Jason curses loudly. Stubhy looks irritated.

12:36 pm

The Lucky Van stops at another gas station to fuel.

12:47 pm

The Lucky van is back on the road.

3:00 pm

The Lucky Van arrives at that night's venue.

3:02 pm

Adam drinks a Coke and smokes a cigarette. Stubhy is on the phone. Ryan sleeps in the back of the van. Jason consults with the venue manager, discussing business. Joe reads a book. Toadie and Tanner unload gear.

3:15 pm

Jason and Joe help unload gear. Adam offers to help, then finds something to eat. Stubhy is still on the phone. Ryan is still asleep.

3:25 pm

Tanner circulates the venue frantically, complaining that he's run out of duct tape and cannot finish setting up the merchandise table. He is wearing a floral print dress, combat boots and an orange camouflage hunter's cap with the price tag still attached. Venue employees eye him curiously.

4:22 pm

Sound check.

4:49 pm

Ryan opens a bottle of vodka and coaxes Adam, who wishes to refrain from drinking, into a single toast.

5:15 pm

Ryan and Adam loudly complain that they are out of vodka. Joe opens a case of Budweiser.

5:32 pm

Joe takes off all of his clothes and dresses himself in a garbage bag and a baseball cap with an oversized brim that protrudes one foot over his forehead and demands that everyone refer to him as Mrs. Rosie O'Donnell.

6:15 pm

Members of the local opening act become concerned after Ryan smashes a martini glass over his head, thereafter attempting to flush the broken pieces of glass down the dressing room toilet.

8:35 pm

Stubhy scowls and becomes despondent after learning that there is no more Jagermeister.

8:47 pm

Tanner upsets a girl at the merchandise table when he compares her appearance to that of Hall and or Oates.

9:02 pm

Shortly before show time, Joe becomes frustrated by the fact that he's drunk too much Jagermeister. He begins barking orders at his bandmates and others gathered backstage, unaware that he is still wearing a garbage bag now torn in several unsightly places and spotted with several unsightly stains.

9:20 pm

Joe is dressed and the band takes the stage, greeted by the sonorous applause and cheers of anxious fans.

Philadelphia

"To Betsy Ross! The original whore of Babylon!" Ryan shouted, raising his glass.

"Is this Babylon?" someone asked.

"This is Philadelphia!" said another voice.

We raised our glasses, tilted our wrists and slammed our glasses back upon the bar.

The bartender gave us a stern look of disapproval. We were well into the post-show revelry, and the employees of The Chevy Grill, a smaller, more intimate club than the larger Trocadero nearby, were visibly displeased. A number of fans had joined us as we gathered around the bar, drinking and shouting and raising our glasses in various cheers. This seemed to make the bartender uneasy, and he eyed us with considerable disdain.

When a glass broke a short time later, the bartender, eager to flex his authority, informed us that our service had been suspended indefinitely.

Adam caught sight of Ryan emerging from the bathroom, victorious, trailed by the blonde. Adam turned to her boyfriend and swept him into another orgy of Sambuca shots that stood forgotten on the bar, served prior to the bartender's suspension. Soon the poor fellow, marked by a Cro-Magnon jaw, Neanderthal forehead, California surfer hair and a meager command of the English language, fell into a stupor incapable of recognizing his girlfriend's infidelity.

Ryan stepped outside and hailed this unfortunate soul a taxi. The man thanked him with uncertain words, and Ryan smiled, closed the car door and tapped the trunk twice to send the cab off.

As Adam followed Ryan outside, a beefy bouncer stuck out an arm embossed with scars, meat and chains.

"What do you think you're doing?" he demanded.

"Leaving," Adam said. "The bartender's a communist."

"Where are you going with that stool?"

"Is this yours?" Adam asked, looking at the article in his hands. "The bartender, he hates this place. Asked me to throw it through the window. Says this bar is part of the military industrial complex. He showed me a pamphlet."

The bouncer frowned, squinting his eyes.

"Either he hates this place or he hates himself. Those tattoos on his arms suck," Adam said.

The bouncer took the stool from Adam.

Next Adam made his way to a bar across the street where he hoped to purchase a supply of beer for the hotel. Tanner and I watched him through the Chevy Grill's window and, finishing our drinks, we made our way outside to wait with Ryan.

Several minutes later Stubhy approached us and suggested that we retrieve Adam from the bar.

"Christ," Ryan said. "Let's hope we don't find him tied up in a gimp mask in the basement again."

We crossed the street and entered the tattered remains of a bar marred with splintering floorboards stained with unwanted memories and sticky with the tears of drunken regret. A broken pinball machine stood in the corner, a relic of an ancient rebellion now impotent and forgotten, its lights dark, its silver balls, bells, sirens, bumpers, whistles and glittering stimulation silent and draped in dust and soot.

Scattered along the bar were the remnants of a better time still clinging to a youth that had long ago passed them by. Interspersed among their rank was a younger generation unable to see their future in these token figures and smashed mirrors. And Adam, yellow t-shirt, gelled hair, swaggering features, chain-smoking innocence, indifferent or wholly naïve, sat one among their number, a tall can of Pabst Blue Ribbon before him and two shopping bags of beer 'to-go' at his right.

I heard Adam arguing, his voice earnest and pleading.

"All I'm saying is that women like a shallow guy when he's flattering," Adam said.

"Yep. You got that right," said the man sitting next to him. This man wore a dirtied orange trucker's cap replete with stained ventilation netting in the back, the hair beneath thick and wet and freckled with dandruff. "That's why feminism doesn't work. It's why women will take the long way to walk past a construction site to hear the whistles and the cat calls. They like the attention and the flattery."

"It's how they know who they are to other men," Adam added.

"You got that right, my man. You're absolutely right on the fucking money," the man said.

"Yeah, well, asking Adam for insight on women is like conferring with the Dalai Lama on the purchase of guns and cocaine," Stubhy said, coming up behind them.

Adam turned to eye Stubhy over his shoulder. Turning back to his new friend, he said, "And Mr. Don Juan's survived abortion is now going to enlighten us on the wonders of the female psyche. Prepare to be underwhelmed."

Without bothering to respond, Stubhy thrust his arm between Adam and his audience, grabbed the two bags of beer and turned and ran out into the street, nearly shouldering the bouncer out of the doorway. He passed Ryan outside who, along with the blonde still at his side, had become distracted with two more female fans. I overheard our hotel address and room numbers as I stood nearby.

Adam fell from his seat in his attempt to seize Stubhy's arm and proceeded to clamber after him out of the doorway. He made several steps into the night air before another balding, neck-less bouncer arrested his way.

"Hey!" the bouncer shouted, holding out his arm. "You can't have an opened drink out here on the street! Take it back inside!"

Stymied, Adam turned and looked him up and down once.

"Do they just breed you all for this job or what?" he asked. "How do they get a Manatee to fuck a retarded Ox anyway? Are there roofies involved?"

"Take it back inside!" the man shouted.

"Relax, it's only half-full."

"I don't care if it's half-empty! Take it back inside!"

Adam eyed him closely and glanced at Stubhy, who smiled at him from the corner and held up the bag of beers.

Relenting, he stepped back across the threshold.

"You're a pessimist," he said. He finished his beer in one long swill and slammed the empty can down upon the glass of the forgotten pinball machine, causing it to jump to life for a brief moment. "You're going to die young."

The previous day Lucky Boys Confusion had played an afternoon show in Buffalo, New York. Because there is little of interest in Buffalo outside of a Lucky Boys Confusion concert and their fans, we drove to Philadelphia immediately after the show, intent on spending two nights in a city with more vitality and attraction.

The first night had been fairly quiet with the exception of a death threat launched at Tanner from a man waiting in line behind him at the movie theater. Things had been pretty mundane again the following afternoon until Tanner incited Adam's fury after tossing his luggage on top of the portable DVD player. To punish him, Adam had thrown Tanner into the shower, dousing him with cold water and holding him under the spray until he had been sufficiently reprimanded.

Unfortunately for Tanner, the clothes he had been wearing were his last clean set, and so Tanner was forced to spoil his afternoon doing laundry. He had scavenged for quarters, digging through his backpack and other people's pockets after locating some old detergent at the bottom of his suitcase.

The self-use laundry facilities were located on our floor, several doors down from Tanner and Toadie's room and just around the corner from the vending machines. With no clean or dry clothes to his name, Tanner had begun his first load of laundry clad only in boxer shorts and combat boots.

Adam accompanied him to the laundry room, intending to use the vending machines to secure a fresh Coke and thinking nothing of Tanner's unique appearance. As he leaned against the set of front-loading dryers, one stacked upon the other, Adam amused himself by watching Tanner struggle with his clothes, cursing and muttering as he crammed sock upon jean upon shirt upon Fruit-of-the-Loom boxer brief into the machine, fingering damp and fetid stains that had grown foul in the moist greenhouse of his suitcase.

Tanner had already consumed the better portion of a six-pack of Bud Light before beginning his laundry room labor, and when he had nearly finished, he turned to Adam and said, "I have to piss."

"Well," Adam said, considering the situation. "I suppose you *could* finish up here and go back to the room. You might have to wait while someone takes a shower or uses the toilet. Perhaps number two. Perhaps Ryan." He paused, letting this unsavory suggestion settle into Tanner's mind. "*Or*, you could just piss in this bottom dryer here and save yourself the trouble," he said, taking a step backward and swinging open the door of the lowermost dryer.

"Aw, yeah! Then I wouldn't have to go back to the room!"

Adam smiled, nodding. "That's the idea."

Tanner eagerly approached the open dryer and exposed himself to its warm interior. He sighed with relief as Adam kept watch along the corridor, hoping that someone would approach.

At the same moment that Tanner began showering the inside of the engaged electrical appliance with a powerful stream of urine, an elderly couple, the woman limping slightly and holding a cane in one hand and her husband's hand in the other, shuffled around the corner. Their approach was slow and methodical, and Adam nodded as they came near enough to see into the small, doorless alcove of the laundry room. They peered inside as they passed and saw Tanner, his waist concealed by the opened door of the dryer, his head craned skyward, his mouth agape, his eyes closed. They heard him sigh, seeming to derive too much pleasure from his domestic labor. The couple, either confused or indifferent, looked at Adam and smiled.

"He's very religious," Adam said.

They smiled and nodded, perhaps not hearing him, perhaps discerning logic. They then proceeded down the hall and disappeared into a nearby room.

Tanner finished unaware of their presence, slammed the door of the dryer shut and staggered several steps back to his business at the washer.

"Success!" he exclaimed several moments later, tossing in too little soap and starting the rush of water. "But these I'm just going to dry now so I have something to wear," he said, holding in his hands the sodden clothes from earlier. "It's not like they're dirty. They're just a little wet."

Adam watched him, curious.

Tanner approached the dryers and loaded the garments into the top compartment, their water-soaked weight slapping the metal surface and shifting the unit slightly. He then produced three quarters, filled the slots and cast his money into the darkness behind.

He depressed the start button and heard the mechanical whirring of the dryer begin its cycle.

As he turned to leave and released the button, the whirring stopped.

"What the fuck?"

He turned back to the machine and depressed the button again. He held it in, heard the cycle begin once more, released it, and was again met with silence.

"What the fuck is wrong with this piece of shit?"

Adam watched.

Tanner shook the machine, barely displacing its weight, and depressed the button once more. This time he held it for several seconds before he released and was again confounded by the silence that followed.

"Goddamnit!" he shouted, kicking the bottom machine with the toe of his boot. "Start!"

Again he pressed; again he failed.

"Fuck *you*!"

Again.

"Looks like it's broken," Adam said.

Tanner stood before the dryers, blond Mohawk, red plaid boxer shorts, weather-beaten black combat boots, tattoo.

"What the fuck? I just wasted seventy-five cents!"

Frustrated, he flung open the door, conscious to slam it hard against the wall. Next he opened the bottom dryer door, again conscious to make his frustration apparent.

Adam was silent.

"Now I'm going to have to find three more quarters!" he complained, drawing his wet clothes from out of the top dryer and throwing them into the seeming vacancy of the bottom one. "These were all the quarters I could find! Now I'm going to have to find some more quarters to dry the clothes that I just put into the washer!" he continued, depositing his last three quarters into the bottom slots, pushing them into the invisible metal abyss, turning the dial to high heat and depressing the start button. "It's fucking bullshit! I ought to get reimbursed!"

This time he heard the machine start and, holding his breath, he released the button and heard the machine continue.

He gave another sigh of relief and said, "Thank *God*, dude. If that one didn't work then I wasn't going to have any clean clothes for hours."

Adam nodded his head in agreement.

During the interim of Tanner's laundry room drama, Jason, Toadie and Joe had arrived to the room. Seeing Tanner enter, Jason laughed, while Toadie merely shrugged, as though the answer to Tanner's odd behavior and appearance rested in his name alone. Joe eyed him up and down and said, "You should have red boots with those shorts," before turning back to the television.

"What the fuck is going on with you today, Tanner?" Jason asked.

"*Adam!*" Tanner shouted, considering this answer enough. He rummaged through his backpack, searching for his wallet.

"I had to discipline him after he almost broke the DVD player," Adam said.

Jason nodded understanding. "And so now he's wandering the halls like Tarzan's bastard son because?"

"Oh, he's doing laundry," Adam said, and waited.

"That's right! Because this fucker threw me into a shower!"

"Is anyone in the bathroom?" Toadie asked, getting up.

"Oh," Tanner said, turning to everyone. "And listen, if you're going to do laundry, don't anybody use the bottom dry—"

Somewhere inside Tanner's mind a small synapse firing a charge of no less or greater measure than the multitudinous others sharing the same network of consciousness at that same moment became a thunderous clap of significance, its small task bearing the significance of epiphany and an apocalyptic fury of implications. It caught his words in his throat, seized his diaphragm and arrested his movements as he realized that he had just thrown his clothes into a dryer filled with his own piss.

"Oh *shit!*"

The crowd in the lobby was tired. They carried their daylong travels heavily upon them. The professional hospitality of well-trained staff and the immediate promise of a clean and comfortable room had begun to ease the irritations of parents who slowly became aware of their summertime vacation. Their children, indifferent to their parents' exhaustion and restless from the confines of cars and airline cabins, discovered renewed vigor in visions of pool water, bouncing beds and room service ice cream sundaes.

Into this contemporary Rockwellian portrait came a soft sound not unfamiliar to the ears of this congregation, a sound hardly registered against the common, gentle din of a hotel lobby. Perhaps the peripheral awareness of one or more of those gathered in the soft quiescence of the lobby heard it, marked it and promptly dismissed it. Yet had those few attentive ears possessed a greater prescient disposition, then the chime of the elevator heralding another arrival might have disturbed their complacency with the touch of something wicked emerging from some primordial ether, some rift in time spanning countless horizons of space to deposit a Neanderthal bastard into their midst, a discarded mistake from a vengeful God, a flaming saber to assail their fragile security.

And so Tanner rounded the corner, Viking, Visigoth, Aztec, Mongol, black boots, boxer shorts, black studded leather belt, Mohawk, topless.

The crowd fell silent, shuddering against a cold wind. Maternal hands drew children near, paternal chests inflated, innocent eyes fell transfixed.

Tucked into the leather belt slung awkwardly about his almost naked waist was Tanner's billfold. Bypassing waiting patrons who swallowed their grievances in the throes of their confusion, Tanner approached the counter, withdrew his wallet and produced several bills.

"Yo, can I get some coins for laundry?"

The woman at the counter smiled, her eyes meeting his across the protruding platform of her chest. They sank slowly downward and salaciously imbibed Tanner's stark figure.

"Hello there, sugar. What can I help you with?"

"I, uh, just need some quarters … Please."

"And what, if you don't mind me asking, do you need this change for?" she asked. "I hope it's not to cover that creamy white chest of yours."

Tanner's creamy white chest flushed. "I just need them for laundry," he said. "I'm doing laundry."

"Are you now?" the woman asked. "And are *all* of your other clothes in the wash already?"

She hadn't yet taken his money or begun to retrieve his change.

"Uh-huh. I had some problems with the dryer upstairs."

"Did you now?" she said. She waited a moment longer and then reached a flirtatious hand out to Tanner, smiling coquettishly as she gingerly took his money.

"My friend threw me into the shower with my clothes on," Tanner said.

"Oh!" she exclaimed, starting to laugh in a chortling, full-body heave that seemed to shake every surface of her overlarge but seemingly well-placed figure. "With friends like *that*, huh, sugar?" she said, still laughing.

"Yeah."

"You and your friends must have started the party early, then," she said, raising one hand and then tilting her wrist.

"Sort of, yeah," Tanner said, smiling, still flushing.

"It's not too often that we get people walking around the hotel in their skivvies this early in the afternoon," she said, her eyes sliding down his torso, pausing at his waist. "Are you all some sort of rock n' rollers?"

Tanner shuffled his feet and looked down. He didn't want to disclose too much. It was bad form to notify hotel staff of their occupation, at least so early in the day.

"Yeah, sort of."

"Well, you ought to hurry your little self back upstairs and finish that laundry so you can get some britches on those cute buns of yours," she said, producing some quarters but withholding them as yet from Tanner.

Tanner flushed anew.

"What floor is it you're on, anyway?"

"Uh, six," Tanner said.

"I'm working late tonight," she said. "And I'll be here long into the morning, so if you and your friends need anything you'll come find me, won't you?"

Tanner stammered. "Yeah, okay." Then quickly added, "Thank you."

She handed him the coins, still smiling playfully into his eyes. Tanner approached her like a wounded street urchin, stepping forward cautiously before snatching the coins from her charitable hand and retreating a few steps.

"You go warm yourself up now," she said.

"Thank you," Tanner repeated before retreating around the corner and disappearing into a waiting elevator car.

We didn't make it to the hotel after leaving the bar with the broken pinball machine. At least, not directly. Instead we drank several beers from Adam's supply as we walked down the street to another bar. There we found some LBC fans still lingering in the vicinity of the concert venue, still reveling in the after-show adrenaline.

Seated with Jason at a table near the back was Adolescent Agenda, one of the opening acts from earlier that night. Backstage following Lucky Boys Confusion's set, Adam had knocked on their dressing room door to invite them out to the bars. After waiting several moments for someone to respond, he had succeeded in forcing the door open and stumbled in upon them as they sat around a small table drinking Pepsi Cola from several two liter bottles. In their hands they each held a fanned set of cards, and before them lay a strange tapestry of squares resembling a tarot card prophesy.

Adam stopped and looked confoundedly about him.

"What the fuck?" he asked no one in particular.

From a small stereo in the corner came the gentle chorus of Lionel Ritchie singing "All Night Long."

They looked at Adam, shades of guilt and innocence clouding their expressions.

"Hey, Adam," one of them said. "What's up?"

A red-headed girl in a black halter top walked up behind Adam and looked over his shoulder.

"Hey," she said. "What's going on in here?"

Adam turned on his heels and took a step toward her, filling her field of vision and urging her backward and away from the door.

"Nothing," he said. "Nothing. Just typical backstage rock n' roll stuff."

He pressed toward her as he spoke so that she had no choice but to retreat several steps.

"It looked like they were," she began.

"Lies! All lies!" Adam said. "You're drunk! It was the lighting!"

Adam then grabbed her shoulders and spun her around, pointing across the way to where Ryan was touching his lighter to a bra that hung from the end of Joe's guitar. Joe was giggling and playing "Like a Virgin" while a blond haired girl, ostensibly the bra's owner, stood before them and watched.

"Look," Adam said. "They need you."

Before she could respond, Adam turned and charged back into the band's dressing room, slamming the door behind him.

"Why'd you tell her," one of them began, but he was cut short as Adam charged forward and scattered their cards from the table, turning them into an explosion of confetti. The band leaned back in their chairs, exclaiming, "Hey! What the fuck are you doing?" as Adam upended the table, sending the remaining cards and all of their drinks careening across the room.

"You're playing *Magic* backstage after a *show!*" Adam shouted. "What the fuck is *wrong* with you?"

Adam looked to the smaller table against the wall. The small stereo there was still playing Lionel Ritchie. His frustration turned his face a shade of red that seemed to threaten an impending stroke. Adam approached the stereo and yanked the cord from the wall, thereafter knocking the radio to the floor for good measure.

"Adam," one of them said. "We were listening to that."

Adam pointed an accusatory finger at them as they sat in chairs around the empty space where there had recently been a table. "You signed up to come out on a rock n' roll tour with us."

"We were just," one began again, but fell silent, ashamed.

"I had to lie to that girl, you know," Adam said. "You owe her an apology."

"But we weren't doing anything wrong."

"Nothing wrong! You've turned what should be a house of iniquity into a den of—of *propriety!*" Adam said, spitting the last word from the back of his throat, dredging it up from some foul recess within him.

"But you didn't have to do all of that," one of them said, gesturing to the mess about them.

"Get your things. You're coming with us. You're going to start acting a little more like a rock band and a little less like James Taylor," Adam had said. "And don't let me catch you playing that shit again or by God we'll relegate you to Tanner Detail."

At the mention of this the band had become quiet.

'Tanner Detail,' as it was called, entailed traveling with Tanner between cities, rooming with him and chaperoning him at night out to the bars and back at the hotel, regardless of groupies or other obligations. Of paramount importance to the 'Tanner Detail' process was Tanner's complete ignorance of its existence. Penalty for transgressing this code of silence or violating any other relevant rules was a longer sentence. No one had ever revealed its existence to Tanner, but some had made the unfortunate error of extending their sentence. This usually happened only once before the lesson was learned. The last ones to incur this particular extension, Logan Square, had left Tanner alone late one night, considering him capable enough to look after himself. They were subsequently punished with having to pay Tanner's bail early the next morning.

When leaving the police station, Tanner had turned and shouted over his shoulder, "Thanks for the five-hundred dollar breakfast, assholes!" at which point Tanner was detained further and released only on behalf of Logan Square's lead singer's diplomatic efforts, who assured the Oakland police department that Tanner's apology was sincere and promised them that they would hear nothing more from him in the future.

Leaving the police station for the second time, Tanner had muttered to Brad, "Jail sucks. My ass is so fucking sore. They made me sit on that concrete bench all fucking night."

After Adam disappeared to find details about our next destination that evening, Adolescent Agenda had found their way to the bar where they began trying to exhibit the sort of rock n' roll manners commensurate with their title. When Adam saw them and approached their table, he was in good cheer and was contrite for having so vehemently chastised them earlier.

"Hey! Look at you guys," he said. "Out drinking in the bars and not a goddamned bottle of Pepsi in sight! Good job!"

"*Do* they have Pepsi here?" one asked.

Across the bar Stubhy stood waiting to order a drink when a woman tapped him on the shoulder. He turned to face an older woman not unattractive but approaching the latter half of middle age, ready to crest the final summit of her youth and begin her final descent to the grave while clinging ungracefully to a manufactured ideal of youthful beauty.

"Do you know what time it is?" she asked.

Stubhy looked her up and down once and said, "Almost too late. *Carpe diem*, for Christ's sake. Your time's almost up."

The woman giggled. "No! It's time I bought you a drink! My son loves your music. We just came from the concert."

Stubhy looked behind her. "You're son?"

"No, no, he's not here. He's only fourteen. His stepfather took him down the street to get something to eat," she said, smiling up at Stubhy.

She then became excited, and turning so that she looked at him over her shoulder, she pushed her still firm and compact butt out toward Stubby. "Look!" she exclaimed, raising the hem of her shirt and sliding the waist of her jeans down to reveal a soft space of skin where, scrawled in black cursive lettering just above her right butt cheek, was Stubby's full name.

Stubby stared in disbelief.

"You got a tattoo of my *name?*" he said.

"That's right!" she said. "Let me buy you a drink."

She turned to face Stubby once more, her clothes falling back to cover most of the flesh of her lower back. She walked past him and leaned onto the bar. His eyes followed her, admiring the space now concealed by the thin fabric of her shirt and the tight denim of her jeans.

He let her buy the first round, and the second one after that.

In the short time that elapsed between their introduction and our departure from the bar, Stubby learned that Jasmine, thirty-nine, worked as a dancer in a strip club on the other side of the city. She invited Stubby and the rest of us to her club where she promised to provide us VIP treatment.

"Finish your drinks," Adam said to Adolescent Agenda after learning of our next destination. "We're going somewhere else."

"Where are we going?" one asked.

"Someplace full of insecure women looking for approval. You'll like it."

"Art school?"

Nine of us piled into The Lucky Van, and Adolescent Agenda rode in their own van. As we pulled away, I saw Ryan's blonde emerge from the bar. She seemed to be in search of Ryan, and when she spied The Lucky Van as it passed, a shadow of rejection fell across her face.

Stubby and Jasmine kept to themselves in the rear of the van and became better acquainted, their interest in each other disturbed only when Jason called to Jasmine from the driver's seat to ask for directions. Two benches ahead of them, Ryan,

Toadie and Tanner insulated themselves in their own private discussion, plotting something. I sat with Adam and Joe on a bench ahead of them.

Joe and I spoke about the plausibility that women could soak tampons in liquor, insert them and become drunk. In support of the theory I posited that the legend of witches riding broomsticks was derived from a custom in which women would smear hallucinogenic materials on sticks—often broomsticks—and then rub them between their legs, seeking a more porous and discreet region by which to ingest the material. Joe then proposed that this could mean that domesticity is a boredom that drives women to drugs, and he offered valium and vicodin as modern-day substitutes that don't carry the threat of splinters.

Adam, trying to ignore us, finally said to Jason, "If we don't separate Derek and Joe, the strippers are going to think we're from some private liberal arts college instead of a rock band. Why does it seem like Stubhy, Ryan, Jason and I are the only ones trying to preserve our dignity on this tour?"

Joe was about to protest when his phone rang. He looked at the call ID, clenched his teeth and promptly rejected the call.

"There's nothing more punk rock than vodka-soaked tampons," I asserted on Joe's behalf. "And you've always talked about getting a sex change anyway."

Jason turned on the radio and found Men at Work singing "Who Can It Be Now" and turned up the volume. Adam folded his arms across his chest and glared out the window.

"If a sex change would put me in better company, then I might," he said.

A brunette giggled from the passenger seat next to Jason and then fell silent once more, looking nervously at Jason to see if she'd done something wrong. No one remembered inviting her, but she was attractive. She been at the bar, and when she had taken a seat in the van as we left, no one protested.

We soon arrived at The Pink Slip, and when Jasmine exited the van, her face paled and her enthusiasm faltered. Toadie looked at her and asked if she was okay.

She raised her index finger in the air as though testing the wind, motioned as if to say something and then keeled over and vomited onto the dark pavement.

Stubhy looked down at her, his own enthusiasm fading, and regarded his shoes, before clean, now spattered with traces of partially digested hotdog and fries and vodka martini. He appeared to wonder whether there was such a thing as karma.

"Hey, you bastards!" Tanner said, standing in the doorway of the van, preparing to jump to the ground. "Where the fuck are all the naked girls at?"

Toadie started to call to him, "Tanner! Don't—" but Tanner had already begun to lunge forward and so there was no time for him to register Toadie's warning, much less dismiss it with his customary indifference.

Tanner landed squarely in Jasmine's puddle, splattering more of the material onto Stubhy and Jasmine's ankles than his own. Stubhy looked at Tanner with silent contempt, and when Tanner started to apologize, Stubhy's eyes were enough to make him stop before he had finished. Jasmine mitigated the tension by starting to retch again, and Stubhy rolled his eyes and ushered her to the rear of the van where her regurgitation would be better concealed and out of Tanner's way.

While Stubhy nursed Jasmine behind the van, the prospect of arriving to VIP treatment became less likely. The sound of full-body heaves coupled with the dried pieces of food and traces of bile at her mouth made Jasmine seem incapable of leading a convincing campaign on our behalf. However this didn't bother Ryan, Toadie and Tanner, who had devised a means of their own to garner the strippers' favor.

"Where are your sunglasses?" Ryan asked Adam.

"In the van. Why?"

But Ryan was already climbing back inside of the van, and he emerged a moment later with Adam's dark RayBan's held aloft.

"Put these on," Ryan said to Tanner. "And wear this coat," he said, handing him a white sport coat. The coat was big on Tanner's smaller frame but not so big that it looked conspicuous.

"Only fasten one button," Toadie said as he fixed Tanner's hair so that the appearance of his disheveled Mohawk looked slightly more refined.

"And you need a cigarette. Keep one in your mouth at all times, sort of hanging out to the side like Humphrey Bogart," Ryan said. "Even if it's not lit and you're not smoking, keep one there. It helps you look dapper and indifferent. You can't look nervous or at all uncomfortable. You need to look jaded."

"And speak as little as possible," Toadie said, handing Tanner a cigarette. "You need to be mysterious."

"But you need to act like an asshole—an aloof asshole," Ryan said. "That's what rock stars are. You think you can handle that?"

"No!" Tanner shouted, erupting with effusive and dramatic gesticulations. "Fuck that! I don't want to act like an asshole!"

Ryan considered.

"Okay, forget it. Just act like yourself."

"Asshole," Tanner said. "You don't need to tell me that."

When Ryan approached to tell us that they were going to pass Tanner off as a famous recording artist known as Lil' Tanner-D, with Ryan and Toadie acting as his bodyguards and Jason as his manager, I asked him why they would choose Tanner, of all people, to be their model celebrity.

"I mean, he doesn't exactly exude that sort of persona," I said.

"That's exactly it," Ryan said. "Do you want to climb Mount Everest or the landfill behind your house? Easy challenges aren't worth the time. Passing Tanner off as a virile celebrity is Everest."

"Hey!" Tanner shouted from behind us. "My clothes don't still smell like piss, do they?"

Ryan smiled. "You guys go in ahead of us and get a few tables. But don't sit too close to the main stage—that's where we're going."

Adam retrieved Adolescent Agenda from their van, and all of us, Adolescent Agenda, Adam, Joe, the brunette and I entered The Pink Slip.

We passed through the velvet curtain beyond the foyer where a beefy bouncer checked your ID and took your money.

Inside we were greeted with the same curious smell common to every strip club, in every city, in every state. It is an aroma at once aromatic, perhaps spiced with the pheromones and perfume from the skin of the young girls parading about the room in naked splendor, and at once repulsive for the fear of what might lie beneath, like the smell of a toilet mistaken for a freshly baked casserole.

The dim red and blue lighting inside The Pink Slip better concealed the occasional Caesarian scars, stretch marks, cellulite and cigarette burns, while the loud and thumping music carried the women through their wanton capering about poles and laps and stage. Women sashayed through the pleasant lights, weaving with serpentine fluidity about the tables and the eager, salivating patrons beseeching them with stupid, rapacious grins. They walked with an air of regality and repulsion, their legs tapering into high heels, their gait cool and commanding, their eyes cast down upon the men whose desires were requited only when their money was visible.

When we took our seats along the wall some distance from the center stage, Adolescent Agenda's guitarist leaned over to Adam and said, in all seriousness, "Adam, these girls seem to be taking their clothes off."

Joe, seated near enough to overhear this, turned a confused look to Adam.

Adam shook his head and laughed. "Where the fuck did you come from? If Derek puts that line in the book people are going to think he's an unimaginative hack."

"In Nick's defense," I said. "People are probably going to think that anyway."

"He's writing a book?" Nick asked.

"It's a children's book," Adam said. "So this is called a strip club. This is where women take off their clothes for money to piss off their fathers."

"How does that piss off their fathers?"

"Never mind," Adam said, waving his hand. "These girls are sort of free-falling. You might catch one for the night, but you have to let them go in the morning. They don't do well in captivity."

Nick looked about the room in astonishment, and the cocktail waitress appeared.

Shortly after receiving our drinks, our attention turned toward the entrance. We saw Tanner followed by Toadie and Ryan as they emerged through the velvet curtains. All three wore dark sunglasses, and Tanner sported the white sport coat Ryan had given him earlier. They had taken greater care to style Tanner's hair with some gel from Jasmine's purse, and a cigarette hung from the corner of his mouth. Tanner said nothing as he stopped just inside, Ryan and Toadie standing to either side of him. They were dressed in black sport coats they had retrieved from the Lucky Boys Confusion trailer, and their faces were stern, their eyes appearing to scan the premises from behind their dark sunglasses.

The patrons seated nearby could be heard to murmur below the thundering onslaught of Motley Crue's "Girls, Girls, Girls," speculating about this interloper in their midst.

The maitre d, or whatever constituted the maitre d in a classy place like The Pink Slip, which was the same guy who checked your ID and took your money when you entered, offered to escort Lil' Tanner-D and his security personnel to a table near the foot of the main stage. Tanner nodded, surveying the club and its other tables, ignoring us.

"Tanner seems to be playing his part well," I said.

"It's the jacket," Joe said. "You become what you wear."

"Let's not forget that his other clothes were soaking in piss earlier," I cautioned.

Tanner took the seat that the maitre d pulled out from the table, and Toadie and Ryan stood behind him, their arms folded, their faces stolid.

Toadie the roadie was short, stout and aggressive. He had spent his high school years playing hockey, taken out of commission only when a bad check had left him with some permanent injury to his lower back. Unable to play hockey, he had channeled his nervous aggressions into the roadie lifestyle and had made himself an indispensable part of the Lucky Boys Confusion road crew. He was often visible just offstage during performances, ready with guitar changes throughout the set.

Ryan, meanwhile, was the savage in uncomfortable clothes. He was the birth of violence wielding a bone in the air high above his head, ready to bring it crashing down upon the skulls of vanquished foes, the vestigial apparition of all that is brutal, primal and untamable from the American wilderness. On certain nights, when the lighting is right and your eyes are relaxed, you could look to the stage from your place amidst the groundlings and see the shadows play themselves upon his features, casting curious squares of darkness about his skin, his eyes lost in concentration, his chest grunting and beating time, singing some incantation under his breath.

In those moments he seemed the specter of the first native to meet the first European arriving to the North American continent. Painted, brutal, the sentinel of a vast untamed and uncharted world, he was the keeper of that vanished wilderness, its clairvoyant past tattooed upon the paved and mortared air.

'I want a drum head made from human flesh,' Ryan once told me. 'The sound would be massive. It would pound into your chest and stay there like the memory of your first fuck.'

Adam had attracted the attention of a raven-haired stripper named Desire, and I asked him why Jason was not with Tanner. Adam glanced disinterestedly in Tanner's direction and said, returning to the woman seated on his lap, "I don't know."

The waitress returned with another round of drinks, and when she left, Joe gestured toward the entrance. Jason entered, dressed in a black button-up shirt tucked into his black jeans. He wore a red tie and on his face rested a pair of thin wire-rimmed glasses. Under his right arm he carried the three inch binder that he usually guarded in hotel rooms and upon arrival at venues, the one which held all of Lucky Boys Confusion's tour information. Before entering The Pink Slip, Jason had wisely emptied the binder of the important paperwork so that all he carried now was an artificial prop meant to exude authority and responsibility. He was escorted to the front and given a seat beside Lil' Tanner-D.

The first strippers to approach Tanner-D's table were waved off, and Tanner-D instead leaned back in his chair, his arms crossed, and waited while Jason ordered him a drink.

A short time later I saw a blonde approach Tanner-D's table. This time, Tanner engaged her.

"What's your name?" he asked.

"JoAnna."

Tanner looked up at her, inspecting her.

"Lil' Tanner-D," he said. "I'm sure you've heard of me, but don't tell the others I'm here."

"Oh! Sure! Wow!" JoAnna said.

"Thanks," Tanner said, then added, "JoAnna's not much of a stripper name, is it?"

"I'm sorry?" she said.

"Do you mind if I call you JoAnne?"

"I—huh?"

"See, I told you," Tanner said, turning to Jason. "They don't care."

"I don't think that's been determined yet," Jason said.

"They?" JoAnna asked.

"It's all good so long as the name is close. It's like a pronunciation thing, is all," Tanner said, returning to JoAnna. "Right?"

"That's insightful," Jason said. "Sagacious."

"But that's not my name."

Tanner turned back to Jason. "What did you just call me?"

"Sagacious."

"It's JoAnna, not JoAnne."

Tanner turned back to JoAnna. "What?"

"Sagacious isn't an—"

"My name's JoAnna."

"What's the difference?" Tanner demanded.

"It means wise," Jason said.

"The difference is that my parents named me Jo*Anna* and not Jo*Anne*."

"Well, I'm sure they didn't put a lot of thought into it."

"I was being generous," Jason finished.

"Who the fuck are you to say whether my parents put a lot of thought into my name?"

"I'm not!" Tanner protested. "I just mean that they probably didn't have a long debate over whether to name you Jo*Anne* or Jo*Anna*. It's all the same. It's a chick name."

"But now I take it back entirely," Jason added.

71

"A *chick* name? What the fuck kind of shit is that?"

"What?" Tanner said. "I'm just saying, is all. I mean, it's an alright name, I guess. It's just not much of a stripper name."

"There must be an antonym or something," Jason said to himself.

"Maybe you should just forget my name entirely, asshole."

"That was probably going to happen anyway, JoAnne."

"Something like obtuse," Jason said, musing.

"Go fuck yourself, asshole."

"What the fuck did I say?" Tanner asked.

"I doubt you're anybody really famous anyway," she said, walking away.

"Maybe she's the sagacious one," Jason said.

"Fuck her!" Tanner said. "What's her problem anyway?"

When Stubhy finally entered the club, he approached our tables, ignoring Tanner-D and what looked like a small dispute in his direction. He looked annoyed, and after taking a seat next to Joe, he quickly drank the rest of a half-finished cocktail left abandoned on the table in front of him before reaching across the table to retrieve a second drink whose ice had mostly melted. This annoyed Stubhy further, and he cringed not against the bitter alcohol but rather the tepid, tasteless water.

It wasn't worth questioning him about Jasmine. She entered shortly after Stubhy, and we could see her at the side of the stage speaking animatedly with several other strippers. At one point she turned to a brunette to show her the tattoo of Stubhy's name and pointed in our direction. The girl clapped her hands together in front of her face and giggled. Jasmine said something else to her and turned and walked to the DJ stand.

After Stubhy had ordered a fresh drink, Joe briefly explained the Tanner situation.

"But why Tanner?" Stubhy asked. Before Joe could explain, Jasmine joined us and turned the conversation to her.

"Welcome to my second home," she said. There were only the faintest stains on one area of her shirt, and her breath had been freshened by a thorough rinsing of vodka. "I'm going to get some more girls over here for you. They all know who you guys are because of me."

"That tattoo is better than a billboard," Joe said.

Jasmlne giggled, and we heard the opening chords to Lucky Boys Confusion's song "Saturday Night." Hearing it, Jasmine jumped to her feet, exclaiming, "This is my favorite song to dance to!" She then began gyrating her hips and Stubhy's name in a way that would make anyone see past the vomit stains.

After receiving word that Lucky Boys Confusion, Jasmine's favorite band, was seated among our sizeable group, the girls began to swarm, at first circling like vultures about a fresh carcass and then diving toward us.

Several drinks later another blonde approached us. I had seen her talking with Tanner earlier, but not too surprisingly she'd walked away, visibly irritated.

Joe made the first introductions.

"What's your name?" he asked.

She tensed. "JoAnna."

"That's a very sweet name. I once dated a girl named JoAnna," I said. Then, more to myself than to her, I added, "At least I think it was JoAnna. It was either JoAnne or JoAnna, I could never remember which."

JoAnna looked uncomfortable, and after Joe suggested that stripper names are generally more colorful, I said, "So has the ship sailed on that free lap dance, or what? I'm not too into cellulite but my friend Joe here is. And Adam's into back hair, so he might throw a few bucks your way."

JoAnna understandably walked off. Fortunately Star, seated nearby on Nick's lap, didn't hear this exchange. I heard Nick mention that he was in a band, which would have made Adam proud if he'd heard it. He and Stubhy, however, were presently occupied with Jasmine and Desire.

"She was kind of cute," Joe said as JoAnna stalked away.

"You know, it wouldn't kill you to show a little discretion every now and then," I said. "Anyway, God forbid we upset one of the strippers."

"*Dancers*," one said, approaching us. "We're *dancers*."

I looked at Joe, whose eyes pleaded for some discretion on my part.

"My name's Ginnette, and this is Sapphire," she told us as several of her friends and colleagues arrived at our table and joined our company. "And this is Chloe and Porsche."

Some time later Joe had a moment of inspiration. He wanted to relieve Ryan and Toadie of their duty as Tanner's bodyguards. The club had bought their act, and Lil' Tanner-D was even getting free drinks, so there could be no dissolving the act without upsetting a few people, not the least of whom might be the bouncer with arms the size of Tanner's waist. He might make it his business to place some of our heads on stakes out front of The Pink Slip to ward off malevolent spirits, Jasmine's advocacy or not.

Joe turned to Porsche and handed her twenty dollars. "Would you go give that guy sitting up front—who is he?" he asked, pointing in Tanner's direction.

"That's Lil' Tanner-D," she said, sounding proud. "He's some sort of rap star or something."

Joe smiled. "Yeah, he is. Would you go give him a dance and tell him that it's on us? Tell him he's welcome to come join us, too. We'd like to meet him."

"Okay," she said, looking at him queerly. "I'll ask him for you, but those guys usually like to keep to themselves."

"However the pieces fall, I'm sure he'll appreciate the dance," he said.

We watched Porsche approach Tanner and begin to swivel her hips in a maddening and seductive dance that was part current, part rising smoke, part thriving, combusting heat. When she had finished, Porsche leaned into Tanner's ear and pointed in our direction. Tanner turned around to inspect us, and Joe smiled and waved a hand, gesturing for him to come to our tables.

Jason looked skeptical. He leaned toward Tanner and said something. But Tanner then stood, drank the remainder of his drink and slammed it upon the table.

Porsche returned just ahead of Tanner and his small entourage and said, "He's coming, but he's sort of weird."

"Who wants to rock like a party star!" Tanner shouted as he came abreast of our table, visibly startling Porsche.

"No shit! Is that Lil' Tanner-D?" Stubhy said. "What the fuck are you doing here?"

Jasmine eyed Tanner suspiciously. She had been in the back seat of The Lucky Van on our way to the club and hadn't paid much attention to anyone other than Stubhy, but one can only ignore Tanner's presence for so long before it becomes a glaring oversight. Still, he was in costume, ostensibly in character and only when she observed Ryan and Jason did she really make the connection.

"What the fuck are Ryan and Jason doing?" she asked, but Stubhy pinched her and coughed over her next words.

We all raised our glasses and gave our salutations, and Jason pulled a table up to ours, retrieving several chairs so that Tanner-D could sit.

Stubhy leaned into Jasmine's ear and took her into our confidence, and with another round of drinks Joe and I huddled together with Ginnette and Porsche, scheming to distract Tanner-D's bodyguards with two more strippers. Our spoken intention, for the benefit of Ginnette and Porsche's ears, was to find a way to get Tanner-D drunk enough to come back to our hotel to party with us, the idea being that this would give us a good story to tell our friends back home. Our unspoken intention, meanwhile, was to help Ryan and Toadie get laid.

Of course we were also curious to see how many strippers we could take from The Pink Slip. Strippers are a lot like trophies in t-ball: anyboyd who wants one can have one. Only for the sake of ours and the girls' amusement did we construct this elaborate game to conceal the obvious. In this way it was really no different from any ordinary courtship.

"Do you think you could find two more girls who would be willing to distract them?" Joe asked, nodding in Toadie and Ryan's direction. "I mean, two girls who would also be willing to leave with us?"

"Who said that *we* were willing to leave with *you*?" Porsche asked.

"Well," Joe said, considering. "What time do you get off of work?"

Porsche smiled down at Joe and waited. A moment later she broke out in laughter, wrapping her arms around his neck. "We can leave whenever we want to!"

Joe looked at me and smiled. There is a certain finesse in the world of strip clubs, and when a stripper tells you that they can leave whenever they want—which is invariably the truth—this is the clearest indication that your efforts have paid off.

"So how about it?" Joe asked.

"I think so, yeah," Ginnette said. She looked in Jason's direction, who leaned back in his chair, bored and indifferent.

"What about him?" she asked. "You think he's going to let that happen?"

"Only one way to find out," Joe said.

I signaled for Jason's attention, and when he turned his head in our direction, I asked, "Do you mind if we ply Lil' Tanner-D's security with some liquor and tits so we can get Tanner-D to come to a hotel party with us?"

Jason looked at the girls and shrugged. "Yeah, fuck it," he said. "Leave him bound and gagged in the trunk of your car for all I care. The guy's a fucking liability."

I turned back to Ginnette, eyebrows raised.

"Okay," she said. "But you guys aren't going to do that to him, or any other kind of weird sexual shit, are you?"

"No," Joe said. "We're out of duct tape."

Our cab stopped in front of The Pink Slip, and Tanner got in first.

Most of the others had left earlier, Ryan with another blonde, Toadie with the brunette, Stubhy still with Jasmine and Joe with Porsche. Their departure had seemed acceptable at the time, the rest of us believing that we could get a ride in Adolescent Agenda's van. Adam had been too distracted, however, to inform us that Adolescent Agenda had left shortly before Joe took command of The Lucky Van.

Adam could hardly be blamed for this oversight as we had all become preoccupied when Ginnette, Star, Desire and Sapphire availed themselves for body shots. We all took a special delight when Ginnette took repeated turns at Star's body, running her tongue in a slow ascent over her tattoo, losing itself for several moments in its terminus between Star's legs before continuing on to the pool of tequila at her navel.

I followed Tanner into the cab, and Ginnette fell in after me. Behind her were Desire and Adam while Jason took the front seat. The cab driver looked a little dolefully at the five of us crammed into her back seat, and she looked like she was about to tell us to get out when Jason greeted her with a friendly hello. She looked like the sort of woman you'd see in Wal Mart on Sunday morning, riding the motorized scooter down the soft drink aisle and lamenting her diabetes as she picked up a case of Mountain Dew.

"You didn't tell the dispatch that there were six of you," she said.

"We're going to the Sheraton," Jason slurred. "And we're bringing the strippers with us."

The driver didn't laugh but said, "Bringing the show home with you tonight, huh?"

"Something like that," Jason said. "It follows us sometimes."

"Can we smoke in your cab?" Ginnette asked. Her voice was coquettish when she wanted something, and it was now also uncontrollably loud.

"No."

"Then can we drink? Just a little bit? We won't spill," Desire said, her head hitting the back of Jason's seat as the cab pulled out of the parking lot.

"No opened containers in here, sorry," the woman said.

"Just relax until we get to the hotel," Jason said. "There'll be plenty of time and drinks there."

"But how long will that be?" Ginnette asked. "I don't like to wait."

"No drinking in my cab," the driver said. She seemed impervious to feminine sweet talk.

"Aw, dude, I know how it is," Tanner said. His head was lolling back and forth about his shoulders as the cab bounced along the city streets. "I know you can't have that kind of shit in here. It's your job and all."

"That's what it is," the driver said.

"When are we going to get to the hotel?" Desire asked.

"Soon," Jason said.

"That's another thing," Tanner began. "It's got to be a lot of pressure, doing this job. People are always telling you how to drive, rushing you, wanting you to go faster and stuff."

"I wasn't saying that!" Desire shouted. "Christ, you sound like my father!"

"No, I wasn't saying you were. But you know how it is, bro," Tanner said, gently slapping the back of the driver's seat.

Our cabbie looked in the rearview mirror and squinted at Tanner, who didn't notice.

"I mean, c'mon, man, that's got to suck," Tanner continued. "I'm just saying that we're not trying to be like that."

"Okay then. Thank you for that," she said.

Jason, seated beside her, sensed a building tension.

"I wasn't trying to be rude, either," Ginnette said, melting her body further into mine. I believed her sincerity if only because her skirt, short to begin with, drew itself tighter and higher as she shifted.

Trying to change the subject, Jason asked the driver, "How long've you lived in Philadelphia?"

"Yeah, but you know this guy gets a ton of passengers every night, right? So all I'm saying is," Tanner continued, but interrupted himself as he belched in the woman's ear. "Shit, I'm sorry, man," he said, searching in the darkness for the handle to roll down the window.

"Tanner," Jason began, but it was too late.

"All I'm saying," Tanner protested, "is that if this guy picks up a ton of people every night, then he's got to sit here and hear a lot of shit from people, you know? The guy's got to be pretty tired of—"

"You know," the driver said, interrupting him. "I'm a woman."

The car became uncomfortably silent. Adam, having sustained only a partial interest in the exchange, struggled to silence his laughter on Desire's lips.

"Oh. Wait, what?" Tanner stammered. "I'm sorry dude—I mean, I'm sorry."

"Well, you're calling me 'man' and 'dude' and 'guy,'" she said, looking at him in the rearview mirror again. "I was getting the impression that you were trying to be cute."

"No, no I'm not. It's just—I mean I couldn't see you from back here. I just—your hair is short and, you know, you just have this very deep voice."

"Excuse me?"

"Your voice, it's just deep, you know? You sort of sound like, uh …"

"Tanner," Jason said, trying to intercede. "Just let it go."

"No, I'm just saying," Tanner continued earnestly. "She has a womanly voice, but a deep voice, you know? Sort of masculine, like that wrestler Chyna. I mean, you should have heard the voice of this transvestite that our friend accidentally made out with. He sounded just like a woman and he, she, it, whatever, just talked like—"

We were all suddenly thrown forward in our seats as the cab pitched forward, heaving our stomachs against our chests and engulfing us in a violent screeching of rubber as it was dragged along the pavement. The car then rocked backward, shuddering to a standstill as our driver shouted, "*Get out!*"

"What?"

"You heard me! Get out! Get the fuck out of my cab!"

"What did—?"

"*Now!*"

After a few tense moments in which no one said anything, we silently filed out of the cab and spilled onto the street.

Tanner, the last to exit the cab, slid along the back seat to exit through the passenger side door. Tenacious to the end, he tried once more to explain himself. "All I was saying is that your voice is—"

"Get the fuck out of my cab you little piece of shit!"

Standing outside, ready to close the door, Tanner said, "You sort of remind me of my father. He had a moustache, too."

We quickly found another cab, and for Tanner's sake we made sure that our driver was a man before climbing in.

Our new cabbie, Mickey, powered through the narrow Philadelphia streets like a psychopath high on crystal meth, and he entertained us with his life history, informing us that he had grown up in both Minneapolis and Boston. His accent was a curious mixture of these two places, and it was difficult to keep track of the details as he reminisced about his days as a young boozer in Minneapolis, speaking in a high-pitched voice that might have prompted Tanner to refer to him as a woman if Mickey had left any room for him to interject.

"Eh, yeah, I once got kicked outta this bawr in New York," Micky continued from nowhere. "Yeah I had about a six-pack of Bud and I chrew a pool cue across some guy's face and eh, I got chrown outta the bawr. I don't know if this bawr has a dress code," he said, gesturing out of the window with one hand while the one on the steering wheel sent the car careening up onto the sidewalk as we screamed past what appeared, in the blur of passing lights, to be a bar. "But the last time I went 'dere I had a cardboawrd box on my head and, uh, they wouldn't let me in ... Hey, you guys don't happen to smoke, do ya?"

Micky dropped us off at the Sheraton, and because he seemed to have taken a liking to us, he refused to accept any money. I've wondered, in the time since, if Mickey in fact ever made any money from his fares or if he was merely some crazed Samaritan with a sizeable inheritance who taxied people around the city solely for the benefit of their company to listen to his various stories.

Because he didn't want Mickey to leave empty-handed, Jason ran to The Lucky Van and returned with a copy of each of Lucky Boys Confusion's CD's and a t-shirt, the largest he could find, and wished him well, adding that whenever Lucky Boys played Philadelphia, Mickey would always be added to the guest list and welcomed to a free show.

"Hey, brother," Mickey said in his high-pitched voice. "You guys're awright."

Jason closed the door and Mickey's engine screamed down the driveway, swerving to avoid a young couple walking arm in arm on the sidewalk and nearly clipping a lamppost as he recovered to the right. The cab turned into the street, still accelerating, and disappeared into the night.

The remainder of this night lives in my memory as a strange network of vague associations. It is a drunkard's scrapbook of images and dialogues that play themselves out in my mind with the fluidity of a hand-cranked 35mm picture show pieced together by a dyslexic hand. The passages that follow are my best attempt to arrange them into some semblance of coherency, and I beg the reader's forgiveness if they do not successfully portray for you the erratic strangeness that tends to color a night at a hotel with strippers, liquor and Lucky Boys Confusion.

After watching Mickey depart, Adam, Desire, Ginnette and I made our way upstairs separately from Jason and Tanner, who wandered off in search of food. The girls had no interest in sustenance other than alcohol, and so we thought it best to satiate their need sooner rather than later. "Stripper Fuel," I think Adam called it, and we knew we would find some in Ryan and Joe's room.

Standing outside of their room as we waited for someone to answer Adam's knock, I heard Ryan shout, "Slide, bitches, slide!" This was followed by muffled shouts and giggles.

"What's going on in there?" I asked.

"Ryan's sliding bitches," Adam said.

I nodded, anticipating further explication, but Adam said nothing more as he knocked again. Ginnette and Desire were quiet, anxious under the threat of impending sobriety.

When the door at last opened, Toadie greeted us and swung the door wide. "Come in! Ryan's sliding bitches!"

Adam smiled at me, gestured ahead of him and said, "Bitch sliding."

I entered the room and saw the blonde, naked and seated at the top of a short ramp constructed from the dismantled headboard which now lay with one end on the edge of the mattress and the other several feet out upon the floor. Over this had been lain the wall mirror, slick with a waterslide of beer and sweat. The blonde giggled as she slid backward down the crude construction, her arms up. She impacted with the floor and rolled heels over head, her legs connecting with a floor lamp that had been patiently waiting to fall over.

"Slide, bitches, slide!" Ryan shouted again.

"If a body catch a body falling," Joe began.

"*Sliding!*" Ryan corrected.

"Through the rye!" Joe finished.

"What?" the blonde asked.

"It's a mirror," Toadie shouted from behind me and Ginnette as we passed him.

"Can I try?" Desire asked.

Adam smiled, Ginnette took off her shirt, Toadie handed them each a bottle and Ryan poured more beer onto the slide.

At one point Desire told us how, as a young girl, she hadn't been allowed to drink Coke. Adam was busy mixing their drinks in paper cups, and I thought this might spoil his affections for Desire altogether.

"So it was a health thing? No soda at all?" Toadie asked.

"No," Desire said. "She just said it was Communist. She wouldn't let us drink it or have it in the house."

"Is that what Tiananmen Square was all about? Soft drinks?" Joe asked.

"She said that the red reminded her too much of communist China," Desire explained. "She only let us drink Pepsi. Their label has red, white and blue. American colors."

"So is it a 'no' on the Coke, then?" Adam asked, slightly appalled.

"I don't like my mother," Desire said, smiling. "It's a 'yes.'"

"Just out of curiosity, what does your father drink?" I asked, handing Ginnette another beer.

"Coke. But I try to ignore that. I just think it tastes better. I don't give a shit what my mother thinks. Besides, she's the bitch who married my stepfather."

Shortly after this confession Porsche told us, as she sat curled up in an arm chair, still naked and giggling to herself, that her father had sent her back to Russia to live with her mother when she was thirteen.

"Russia. That sounds cool," Toadie said. "Why'd he do that?"

"Well," she said, temporizing. She gazed into an empty space above her, drawing from her cigarette. "I think they call it 'grand theft auto.'" She exhaled. "That and my stepmother didn't really appreciate me."

"Your stepmother?" Toadie said.

Someone opened a fresh bottle of Bud Light and Porsche giggled. "She chased me with a knife once. But nothing too bad, really."

"She chased you with a *knife*?" Joe said, his laughter abating.

"A butcher knife. She was a pretty good cook."

For no apparent reason, Toadie chose this moment to throw the alarm clock at the television where it impacted and scattered into several small pieces of shrapnel, startling the girls. A true athlete, Toadie had somehow managed to throw the clock hard enough and accurately enough to depress the power button on the television, and the picture came alive. Leaping up he shouted, "Fuck yeah! I didn't think I'd be able to hit it from here!"

Adam, upset, also leaped up. Pointing at the screen, he said, "Look what you did!"

"What?" Toadie asked, looking at the floor. "It's just a fucking alarm clock. Who cares?"

"Not that," Adam said. "Look at the TV! Look at the picture!"

The girls started laughing while the rest of us sat in silence, anticipating something more.

"Shit," Toadie said, genuinely contrite. "I'm sorry. I just wanted to change the subject. It was getting too cathartic in here."

"Well, this is totally fucked-up now," Adam said, still pointing at the television and looking at Toadie as though he were reprimanding a child. "You better hope I'm able to fix it."

Toadie looked at the screen for the first time then, and after a moment he said in a puzzled voice, "I don't think there's anything wrong with it. It's the clock-radio that's broken."

Adam stood before the TV with the remote control, flipping through the channels and shaking his head. "Nope. It's definitely fucked."

The girls giggled some more, watching the changing images. When Adam found MTV, he stopped.

"What're you going to do?" Ryan asked, smiling fiendishly. "It's totally fucked, there's nothing you can do. Toadie ruined it."

Adam sighed. "In my professional opinion, this television is definitely thirsty," he said.

The girls began to giggle harder at this, and their eyes were fixed on the changing pictures on the screen.

"Thirsty?" Toadie said, still inspecting the picture. "What the fuck is wrong with you? What does that even mean?"

"Definitely thirsty," Adam said again. He extended his arm and slowly poured the remainder of his beer onto the innocent television. Some crackling followed, and the picture, before fine, became distorted.

The blonde sat bolt upright and leaned forward, shouting "Oh my God! What are you doing?"

Adam inspected the screen again. "It's still thirsty," he said, ignoring the blonde. He grabbed another opened beer and poured this over the top of the television. The liquid sloshed into the ventilation grating at the rear while some of it spilled down over the screen. The rest of the beer, sticky and foaming, ran down onto the TV stand and the shag below. "These goddamned things are insatiable."

As he poured a third beer onto the unit there was a sound of more popping followed by a soft sizzling, and the picture went completely dark.

Porsche laughed harder, the blonde looked at the darkened screen in stupefied disbelief, Ginnette's head lolled drunkenly upon her shoulder and Desire smiled and looked around the room at all of us, wondering if she should laugh too.

"There," Adam said, turning back to Toadie. "Now get on the phone and tell the front desk they owe us another case of beer because the fucking TV just drank the rest of ours."

Some time after Adam disappeared with Desire, the brunette who had left The Pink Slip with Toadie told us that she had once been incarcerated.

"For what?" Joe asked.

"Because I loved him too much," she said. "So I broke her teeth out."

I saw Toadie shift uncomfortably.

"Ah. That explains it," Ryan said. He seemed to want to clear the room in order to secure some privacy. He and the blonde had become noticeably amorous.

Joe missed this cue, perhaps because he shared the room with Ryan and was used to company or because he had ceased to care about Ryan's raging libido.

"So she was sleeping with your boyfriend?" Joe asked.

"No," the brunette said. "She came out of her house because I was smashing car mirrors. The ones on the doors."

"Why?" Joe asked.

"I guess it was her car," she said, shrugging.

"Wait, you didn't know it was her car?"

"No."

"And she wasn't sleeping with your boyfriend?" Joe asked again.

"No. I told you, I did it because I loved him," she said.

"So you two had a fight?" Joe said, unable to give up without a satisfactory explanation.

"No. He dared me to. He said that I would do it if I loved him."

"See?" Ryan said. "She got what she deserved. Great story. Hey, I wonder what's going on in Stubhy and Jason's room?"

"He said that if I loved him I would go outside and start smashing the rearview mirrors on the cars parked in the street, and so I did," she continued, seemingly annoyed that we would need any more explanation. "And then this girl comes running at me and starts shouting in my face. So I hit her. It was self-defense."

"She hit you first?" I asked.

"No, I hit her first, but after that it was self-defense."

"And you knocked her teeth out?" Toadie asked, impressed.

"It was self-defense," she repeated.

"After you hit her first," Joe said.

"I didn't mean to," she said.

"Hit her?"

"Break her teeth out. But I was only in jail for eight months."

After Porsche suffered a minor panic attack when she thought someone had stolen her purse, Ginnette and I left. The scene with Porsche had threatened to thoroughly displace the mirth, and it had the effect of compelling Toadie and the brunette to leave as well.

Emerging from a curiously long stint in the bathroom, Porsche had shrieked, "Oh my God! Where is my Christian Dior bag?"

"Your what?" Toadie asked.

"Oh my God! Where is it! It's a Christian Dior and I swear to *God* I'll fucking kill the motherfucker that—"

Joe kicked aside a pillow on the floor, and Porsche promptly fell to her knees and clutched the purse to her chest.

"This bag is really valuable. It's a Christian Dior," she said, giggling and wiping away a tear. "I love this bag. And my blackberry's in here."

If I had thought that leaving this company for Ginnette's exclusive company in my own room several floors below would be a step toward improving the overall sanity of my surroundings, I was sadly mistaken. But like most men, I'm not averse to the influence of crazy upon a woman's energy in the dark. However the benefit of a woman's dystrophic eccentricity can soon dissipate once the fun is over, and so I took immediate measures to distance myself from her growing intolerability.

I sought out Jason, considering him to be the best possible source of stability and normalcy. I found him in his and Stubhy's shared room, drunk and listening to music on his computer. After mixing me a drink, he mumbled something, picked up the phone and dialed a long series of numbers.

He looked at me and smiled, and then I heard a faraway voice come from the earpiece as I sat in a chair, enjoying the music and tapping my feet to its rhythm.

"*Pronto! Ciao! Come stai?*" Jason exclaimed, startling me out of my calm.

He listened intently.

"*Come stai?*" he said again.

I heard a long stream of sounds coming through the earpiece again. The voice was feminine, and her words sounded foreign and passionate and almost musical.

"*Che?*" Jason asked.

More words.

"No. No," Jason said.

Another response.

"*Che?*"

I watched, holding my drink still, one eyebrow raised.

"No, no, no," Jason said, shaking his head. "*Che?*"

Again he listened, now closing his eyes and grinning.

"Eh, no," he said when the voice stopped.

The voice became much louder, and I could feel my body quiver as some foreign flame ignited an intrigue and a curiosity not altogether removed from some new exciting arousal. I wanted to hear more of this woman's voice.

When the words seemed to fade, Jason started over again. "*Pronto Ciao! Come stai?*"

The voice rose once more and then abruptly cut off, leaving only silence and the now stale sounds coming from Jason's computer.

"Who was *that?*" I asked. "What just happened? What did they say?"

"I don't know," Jason said, replacing the receiver upon the cradle. "'Hello,' 'how are you' and 'what' is the only Italian I know. I just love the sound of the language. I try to keep them on the line as long as possible just to hear them talk."

"Who do you know that lives in Italy?"

"No one," he said. "I have three phone numbers in Italy and one in France memorized. These poor people—I do this every so often, and when they realize who it is they get pretty pissed. God knows what time it is there when I call."

He turned back to the phone, lifted the receiver and said, "Here, let's call another one."

I turned down the music on the computer and leaned forward, waiting.

When I came upon Adam wandering the hallway, smoking a cigarette and happily tapping some rhythm upon his thighs, his countless wallet chains jingling like a tambourine to the beat, Desire was no longer with him. Ginnette was not with me, and our eyes said enough that we didn't waste time with the details of their particular depravity.

We made our way to Ryan and Joe's room and found the door cracked open. We entered and saw Ryan sitting on the floor before a mirror that had been smashed to pieces. A bottle stood nearby on the floor beside him.

"I thought I could reach in and pull him out," Ryan said without looking up. "That bastard looked like a goddamned madman. I wanted to talk to him."

There were bloodstains on the walls, the dresser and the television, and Ryan had turned the setting sun in the garden painting hanging above the bed into a massive red orb.

"Jesus, dude," Adam said. "How much blood did you lose?"

"Not enough," Ryan said. "I wanted to paint the roses red, too."

I went into the bathroom and saw, scrawled in black mascara across the wall, the words 'I Love Broken Things.'

"Who the fuck wrote this?" I asked.

"Porsche," Ryan said, still looking into his distorted reflection on the floor. "Joe's been following her around. I think he went to go see if they could have sex in the elevator."

"What, is he going to ask for management's permission?"

"He's out of his mind," Adam said. "Those elevator cars are too well lit. Porsche's skin will never hold up under that kind of scrutiny."

"Where's the blonde?" I asked, emerging from the bathroom with a glass.

"I don't know," Ryan said, looking up for the first time. "I think she went to find Ginnette and Desire." Then, shaking his head in discouragement and looking down at his fractured reflection again, he said, "She'll be back."

"Problems?" Adam said, lighting a cigarette.

"She's alright, I guess," Ryan said. "She has an adorable voice. She sounds like she's twelve-years-old. She even sounds cute when she says 'abortion.'"

"So you've already broached the subject," Adam said.

"No, she brought it up. What is it with these chicks taking us into their confidence tonight? Less history more mystery, you know what I mean?"

"I think Toadie's girl has a monopoly on that," Adam said. "It's a good thing Toadie's a hockey player. Ten bucks says he has bruises in the morning."

"But you've missed some of the crazy-ass shit Porsche's been saying," Ryan said, drinking from the bottle.

An hour later and the sun started to spill harsh, unfettered light into the room through parts in the curtains. We were still drunk and somehow still awake.

At some point Joe, Porsche and the blonde had returned. During a lull in the conversation, Porsche had looked toward the light.

"I don't want to do this anymore. I want out, you know? I got into this when I was young and stupid and didn't know any better. I just needed to earn money."

She looked from the light to her beer, her eyes lost, gazing into an amber reflecting pond.

Then she added, "But I like my Christian Dior bags."

She giggled.

The night was over, and we left for our respective rooms for a few short hours of pointless sleep.

That morning I had a headache, and it was bright behind my sunglasses. We stood around The Lucky Van, waiting to leave. Toadie was telling Joe, Ryan, Adam and me that last night he had seen the overweight desk clerk chasing Tanner down the hall, calling him 'sugarbuns' and 'sweetcakes' until they disappeared into Tanner's room.

The details were spotty, and Tanner wasn't talking.

Next Ryan told us how the blonde's personality had changed when they were getting dressed for breakfast.

"All of a sudden she started telling me that she was going to follow us to New York and then down the coast and out west for the rest of the tour. She started talking about coming back to Chicago with me."

"Yikes," Joe said.

"She seemed serious about trying, and I didn't know how to get her to leave. She was starting to sound really crazy. She was talking about how we would be able to party together every night, even once we got back to Chicago."

"How did you get her to give that up?" Adam asked. His voice was raspy and he was smoking another morning cigarette. "Because she sure as hell better not show up in California."

"While she was taking a shower I ran down to the gift shop here in the hotel. It was just opening up, and I bought a ring. Some little trinket for about ten bucks, but it came in a small case."

"What? Why?" Toadie said, shifting his feet.

"Then I went back up to the room to get her, and we came downstairs to the restaurant for breakfast. As we ate, it started to get a little more crowded with people coming down to check out of their rooms and get coffee and breakfast, and so that's when I got down on one knee and asked her to marry me."

"What?" Adam said.

"Holy fuck," Toadie said. "You're shitting me."

Weak and tired, my temples throbbing, I gaped uncomprehendingly at Ryan.

"No joke," Ryan said.

"Wait, wait," Toadie said, waving his hand before him and shaking his head. "The girl was acting weird and clingy, and so you asked her to marry you in the middle of a crowded restaurant?"

"It sounds kind of funny when you put it like that, but—"

"What the fuck is *wrong* with you?" Toadie shouted.

Ryan smiled, and Joe spoke.

"Dude, that's fucking brilliant."

Toadie looked hostilely at Joe. "What the fuck are you talking about? He's lost his fucking mind!"

"You don't understand," Joe said to Toadie. "This girl, she's clinging to Ryan because she knows he's going away. She knows he's going to leave her in a few hours after we pack up. She knows that he's unavailable, knows that he's in a touring fucking rock band, and *that's* why she's clinging to him. But the instant he shows any sign of clinging to *her*, she loses all interest. Suddenly she's no longer attracted to him. It's like salting ice— her interest dissolves."

Adam blew a cloud of smoke up to the sky and said, "I get it."

"She looked at the ring and then she looked at me," Ryan said. "I played it up real professional. Anyone would've thought we were a young couple in love on vacation. People in the restaurant turned toward us, mothers hushed their daughters and whispered to them to watch, hoping for some real Hollywood happily-ever-after moment. And here I was, so fucking hungover that my eyes felt like they were going to burst out of my fucking skull.

"She got really stiff and uncomfortable. I told her that I thought this was a magic turn of fate, that she *should* come out on tour with us. I told her how we could go back to Chicago, I could quit the band and we could get an apartment, just to start with, then later we could get a house. I'd get a job, something nine-to-five, and then we could start a family. She could stay at home and raise the kids. We wouldn't have a lot, I told her, but we'd have each other and we'd be happy. It would be the start of a brand-new life together. This was meant to be.

"I went on like that for a little bit, and she just started to shake her head. You could hear the people around us gasp. I actually felt kind of bad for putting them on. But they helped to make sure that we could leave this morning without a lot of unpleasantness."

"So what did she say? What did she do?" Toadie asked.

"She just sat there, shaking her head and looking at me like I was crazy. Then she put out her cigarette, got up and went out of the restaurant and back up to the room to get her things."

"Jesus. What the fuck did you do?"

"I watched her go, put the ring back in my pocket and finished my breakfast. And hers. They've got a killer eggs Benedict here, if you guys haven't eaten yet. The people near my table actually felt kind of sorry for me. One guy sent me a mimosa, which was cool, as a sort of sympathy drink. And when I went to pay the bill, the waitress told me that it was okay, that it was on the house! I could start doing this more often and eat for free the rest of the tour! I left the waitress a big tip, went back up to the room and she was gone. I packed my things as usual and came down here to wait for you assholes."

Stubhy approached The Lucky Van, toting his suitcase behind him. He was not in good spirits on the best of mornings, much less after a night of heavy drinking and little sleep.

He threw his suitcase into the back of the van.

"What the fuck are you all standing around for?" he asked as he slammed the door. Jason started the van and reviewed the map of the day's route.

"Ryan was telling us about the chick he asked to marry him this morning," Adam said.

Stubhy scowled. "Whatever. Let's get the fuck out of here."

When The Lucky Van was two hours on the road, Adam thought of something.

He turned to Tanner, but he was asleep. Adam shrugged.

Later, at a rest stop three hours on the road, he remembered what he had meant to ask Tanner.

"Hey, did you ever get your other load of laundry from the laundry room?"

Tanner's eyes got wide, his mouth full of vending machine crackers.

"Oh *shit!*"

Red Tape

Lucky Boys Confusion travels in a GMC extended cab van with four benches. It is white. Behind it, in a black trailer, rides the gear for their shows.

The inside of this trailer is interesting because apart from guitars, amplifiers, monitors, drums and crates of merchandise, it is also a traveling armoire of various costumes, namely jackets, shirts and ties. These hang in bags at the rear of the trailer.

Part of the task of writing this book included interviewing my friends with the idea of divining a clearer understanding of their life as professional musicians. If I wanted to unravel the mystery of Lucky Boys Confusion's appeal to such a large contingent of fans from disparate backgrounds, I believed that I should start with how they, as a band, identify themselves.

I have culled most of the following dialogues from conversations I had with Adam and Stubhy while backstage at shows or waiting in bars and hotel lobbies across the country.

"I don't think we have a definable identity," Stubhy said. "We've always had resistance within the band to adopt a certain image, especially from Joe. When we first started, we wanted to fashion ourselves as the band that dresses the same way onstage as we do offstage, and the kids really dug that. I think that might be because one thing kids despise more than their parents is disingenuousness. Something artificial, a lie, becomes a veiled insult to their capacity to uncover it. You have to remember that when we started this band, music was still pulling itself out of the grunge phase. Kids still saw fashion and showmanship as artificial. Ironically, going onstage with the same appearance and the same clothes that we wore offstage became its own image and fashion for us. That was always sort of the irony behind the whole grunge scene, too, I think. As much as they may have tried to avoid it, they were still selling an image. But it hasn't always served us so well."

Adam, Joe, Stubhy, Ryan, Jason (photo: Nabil Elderkin)

"Up until a couple of years ago, about the time of our album *Commitment*, we didn't really have discussions about our image," Adam said. "When we started the band we were all into the same things, and so we naturally gravitated toward a common image. We're different people now, and we've grown apart in some ways. As we started to develop different tastes, it became obvious that we needed to establish some kind of uniformity. It's nothing really contrived, though. Nobody feels like they're being forced out of character. It's a group decision and it reflects our mood and our music at the time."

Jason, Adam, Stubhy, Joe, Ryan. (photo: Huy Doan)

"It's always been sort of an issue with us," Stubhy said later. "Just recently I was talking with Tony from the band Mest, and he said, 'You know what your biggest problem is? People don't know who the hell you are.' And he's right. They don't. I mean, you can't really look at us and tell what kind of music we are beyond the fact that, yeah, we're a rock quintet. But again, that sort of confusion has, in a way, become our identity. And I don't think there are many people who like us for just one song, either. We're not exactly a one-song band. We never had a very big hit, even with Fred Astaire, and it's hard to point to one song and tell people, 'this is what Lucky Boys Confusion sounds like,' because the next song they hear might sound completely different. The people who get to know us, though, know exactly what we're about."

Adam

"Uniformity is sort of important, though," Adam said. "If there isn't some kind of uniform identity, it becomes too confusing to look at. A band also has a certain responsibility to present themselves like a team. It's important for people to look up to the stage and see unity instead of five different individuals. People need to know what you're about."

"What *are* you about?"

Reflecting for a moment, Adam said, "Well, we're not a hipster band. And we're not surfers, we're not cowboys, we're not glam rock—we're just a bunch of suburbanites. Part of our problem is that we haven't niched ourselves into a clearly defined category. That might make it easier to sell records, and that might be one reason why Elektra didn't really know what to do with us. But if it's not genuine, then what's the point? The kids will see through it and then it won't matter how many records you've sold."

Ryan and Stubhy in Detroit, 2005

"We've always wanted to be eclectic and try different things. That's sort of been one of our strengths and one of our weaknesses. A lot of the kids like us for the fact that we try not to do the same thing twice," Stubhy said. "Marketing-wise that's always been a problem because a company wants to know whether we're a 311 band or a Sublime band or a ska band or a pop band or a punk band. We try not to be any single one of those because we want to blend everything together. But I think that's another reason why teenagers enjoy us—we're as spastic and erratic as they are. How many image changes does a teenager go through between their freshman and senior year of high school? Our image changes just as their tastes change, whether it's their food choices, their music, their clothes, their hair, or their hobbies. Eventually you come around to a combination of everything that you went through and everything that you've been through and there it is: a little bit of everything from every year that you've lived, and that's who you are now. That's how I look at our music."

Ryan, Joe, Stubhy, Jason, Adam. (photo: Huy Doan)

"It's not just about what you *are*, I guess," Adam said, "but what you're *not*. But I definitely think that we have a style. I mean, we sell a ton of t-shirts to the kids, so what the hell is that if it's not style or fashion?"

Toadie, "Ronnie the Cabbie" and Adam.

"It is, in a strange sense, like being invisible," Stubhy said late one night. "Okay, people come up to you, they know who you are, they tell you that they love you and your music and your show, they're wearing your t-shirt and they want an autograph. It's all flattering, and they love something that's a piece of you. It's your creation, and that never gets old. But at some point it's like the creation overtakes you. It replaces you. At some point *you* cease to exist and you become your creation's chaperone. It's not really about art imitating life or life imitating art. The art *is* a life, and then where are you? You're Doctor Frankenstein in the shadows. Then people's image of you becomes a prescription and a role you have to fill, and on the road we sort of cut loose and vent our frustrations. It's a pressure cooker that pulls us along."

Tanner. Vending.

Ft. Lauderdale

There was a look of terror in her eyes when I told her that I would have to wait before checking in. Tonight's rooms were reserved under a friend's name, I told her, and he was en route from a performance in a neighboring city.

Noting the apprehension in the desk attendant's face, I added that he and the others were in a band—a rock band. This was hardly necessary, as their occupation would be obvious when they arrived. Subtlety, after all, is not a common feature of rock n' rollers, and their appearance often betrays their occupation.

The time was 9:30.

I smiled.

"Fuses are for bitches!" Ryan shouted as Adam and I stepped from the elevator car onto the fifth floor.

Ryan approached us, trailed by the blonde. Tonight she was giggling but apprehensive as she came near to us. She turned to look behind her and then back up to Ryan and then behind her again in an endless girlhood game of fear and delight.

Ryan's fashionable white-collared shirt was open from the middle of his chest, his were jeans dirty and stained and his hair greasy and disheveled. Despite this appearance and his obvious intake of liquor, he nonetheless exuded an air of dignified composure both stylish and charming. It was his cloak of invincibility, disarming would-be combatants who were either graced by the effect of his boyhood charm or discerned a madness in his appearance.

In his wake the hallway was dark, and Ryan raised his bottle in salute to our arrival.

"What the fuck are you doing?" Adam asked.

"I'm saving the planet!" he said.

The blonde looked up at us and managed a timid smile. She seemed a little more concerned about the doors opening in the darkness behind them. But any opened doors quickly closed again, seeing only visions of the apocalypse in a raving horseman framed by the light at the end of the hall, a silhouette of Revelations hoisting aloft his saber of divine judgment.

"Too much energy wasted on these fucking lights, so I'm taking them out," Ryan continued. To punctuate his words he turned to the fixture beside him and smashed first one and then the other light bulb, using the bottle as the sledgehammer of his environmental justice.

We watched.

"Now for the *coup-de-grace*."

He withdrew a small piece of foil shaped into a tuning fork, and in the now faint light shed by the remaining lamps just near the elevators, he stuck this into the exposed sockets of the smashed light bulbs. There was a large spark accompanied by a soft pop.

The blonde giggled appreciatively.

"I didn't know you were such a passionate environmentalist," I said.

"It's going to become a whole new lifestyle for me. Next it's Greenpeace. I'm going to teach those fuckers a lesson about conserving fossil fuels by using oils from whale fat."

"Whale fat?"

"After that it's the Sierra Club and managing troublesome seal populations by clubbing the babies," he said.

After smashing three more light fixtures, he stood before us in the last vestige of light near the bay of elevators.

"Well," I said. "Are you going to finish the job?"

"I never start anything I can't finish," he said. And, punctual as ever, the floor went dark to a cued cymbal crash.

Later that night, when two members of The Plain White T's stepped from the elevator onto their floor and were met with darkness, they turned to each other, the one saying, "Lucky Boys."

"Don't go to the hotel!" Tanner shouted. He was leaning out of the passenger side window of The Lucky Van. A white tank-top undershirt clung to his sallow torso, and his blond Mohawk, damp and oily, stood at odd angles.

Adam and I were walking back from a nearby bar, having grown tired of waiting for the others to join us.

Adam stopped and spoke to Tanner from the sidewalk. "Why not?"

"The fire alarms went off!" Tanner shouted.

"So what?"

"So don't go back there! It's—just get in the van!"

Adam studied Tanner a moment. "Did *you* set off the fire alarms?"

"What? No! I—it doesn't matter! No!"

"Then what's the problem?"

"Just don't go back to the hotel! Get in the van!"

Adam looked in the direction of the hotel. "We're only two blocks away."

"Why are you guys in the van?" I asked. Once the van was parked at night, it typically stayed parked until it was time to leave the next morning. An extended cab van with trailer in tow isn't conducive to navigating unfamiliar city streets, especially at night, especially with drinks.

Tanner, at least, wasn't driving.

Jason leaned over the steering wheel to peer around Tanner. Less animated and far less panicked than Tanner, he seemed sincere, which gave the situation an added gravity that was lost when Tanner was speaking.

"Seriously, guys. I wouldn't go back there right now," he said.

"But why *not*?" Adam persisted.

"Where are you guys going?" I asked.

"For the last fucking time!" Tanner shouted. "Just get in the fucking van! *Now!*"

Adam shook his head. Tanner could never be allowed to prevail when speaking in such a tone of voice, especially to Adam.

"Whatever, man," Adam said. "We'll see you later."

"Are you going on a beer run?" I asked.

The van sputtered a moment and then trundled away. Jason understood that Tanner had ruined Adam's and my chance at salvation. We were thus left to ourselves, and God speed to us.

"Were there other people in the van?" I asked, turning to Adam.

"I don't know.

"Are those sirens?"

Check-in had proceeded uneventfully. The arrival of Lucky Boys Confusion silently toting their luggage and hangovers through the doorway had seemed unremarkable enough. Harmless, polite and subdued, they had appeared an impotent threat far removed from the urban myths of midnight rock n' roll nihilism.

But it was then only shortly after ten, and the night was still very young.

There had been a subtle indication that this quiescence would not last when, as we walked to our rooms, Adam took an interest in one of the wall-mounted light fixtures lining the hallway and disinterestedly turned the two electric candelabras downward, altering both their appearance and the shadow they cast.

I followed behind Adam, Tanner beside me, all of us silent. Tanner seemed most impressed by this maneuver as he paused to inspect Adam's work, marking his technique by first swinging the structure upright and then back down again. He seemed to admire most the change in lighting this produced, possibly because of its improved proximity to his eye level.

"That's cool," he said to no one in particular.

We pressed onward to our rooms and rest that would be long in coming.

Somewhere, an irreversible switch had been thrown.

*   *   *

Adam and I were greeted by approaching sirens that grew louder until their piercing wail fixed itself before us, stopping in the driveway before our hotel.

"This should be interesting," Adam said.

"I'm not sure that we had enough to drink at the bar," I said. "We might not be sufficiently equipped."

"Nonsense, man, we had plenty. Remember when you made a pass at the cocktail waitress? Something you never would have done if you weren't drunk. She looked like your sister."

"I don't have a sister."

"But if you did ..."

Another police cruiser raced up the driveway and stopped beside the fire truck. An officer emerged and entered the lobby, walking swiftly.

"I don't see any smoke," I said, walking toward the entrance. "Holy *shit*, look at the lobby!"

I turned to my friend and realized that I had spoken to myself. I saw Adam across the street taking no real precautions to conceal himself as he urinated behind a parked car.

Leaving him behind, I walked the rest of the way up the driveway and braced myself for what lay ahead.

The revolving door spun, and I slid silently into the lobby. All around me were people holding children and the hems of bathrobes wrapped against the air-conditioned air, all of them clearly displeased.

I made my way into the crowd, donning a similar visage of hostile disapproval so as not to rouse their suspicions. Several people regarded me with tired, red eyes, and I felt that I would have to be careful with how I would garner first their trust and then their intelligence. I wanted some answers, but a blunder might incite their bloodlust.

I selected a harmless looking man holding an infant and decided to broach the subject.

"So what the fuck is going on here?" I asked him, my voice unintentionally loud and abrasive. I was reminded of Adam's sambuka shots at the bar and guessed that my breath might also betray my overindulgence.

The young child in the man's arms struggled against its father's clutch, toeing a fragile line between a tantrum and tired complacency. The father, exhausted and long unfamiliar with two o'clock in the morning apart from screaming children and tearful repentances before a cloudy bathroom mirror, looked resentfully upon me. His was a world of family and work, occupation and stress, obligation and commitment, and beneath this lay a testosterone regret, a betrayed misgiving that perceived a lie in the ideal he now carried as a standard.

I was his tired accusation, the specter of unshackled youth.

"Excuse me?" he said.

"Is this some sort of a party? Where are the cocktail waitresses, the go-go dancers, the French maids and the strippers?" I leaned conspicuously forward and looked past him to his wife, who stood beside his daughter.

"The fire alarms went off and they called everyone out of their rooms," he said through thin and pale lips.

"Oh," I said, sounding disappointed. "That explains the fire trucks. What with all the police and firemen, I was starting to think this might be some sort of gay disco, you know? Like all we need now are an Indian and a construction worker." I looked him up and down. "Who're you supposed to be?"

He ignored me.

"Nothing wrong with that, though," I continued. "I love the gays. Great rollerbladers. So who started this fire, do you suppose?"

"All they've said is that there was a problem on the fifth floor."

"The fifth, huh? I've been to that floor. Nothing but trouble, city to city. Nothing but miscreants, inbreds and sexual deviants on that floor."

"What?" he said, distracted by the squirming of the child in his arms.

"Yep," I said. "Every last one of 'em."

The child sputtered, and a trickle of spittle, yellow and sticky, issued from the corner of its mouth and fell onto the father's collared polo t-shirt. This upset the man, and with his attention momentarily averted I slipped back into the crowd, disappearing among the disgruntled patrons still waiting to return to their rooms.

As I was selecting another target, there was a loud jarring of metal and glass that roused the dreary assemblage from out of their stupefied complacency. They jostled and shifted and tensed like a herd of wildebeest suddenly aware of a predator in their midst. I turned and saw Adam, laughing, having stumbled while manipulating the confounding metalwork enclosing him in the space of the revolving door.

He righted himself, pushed on and spilled into the lobby. Either entirely oblivious or indifferent to the rising tension of the room, he dusted himself off, shook his leather jacket back over his arms and chuckled to himself. With this unintentionally dramatic entrance, all conversation and agitated murmurings had stopped.

Adam stood upon unsteady feet and looked about him, ingesting his surroundings. Accustomed to the stage and imbued with liquor, he seemed unimpressed by the faces and silent accusations turned upon him. His eyebrows flexed, and he reached into his pocket to retrieve his pack of Parliaments. He withdrew a cigarette and placed it in his mouth. Then, patting his pockets, he asked, "Anyone got a light?"

"Tanner, what the fuck are you doing?" Jason asked as he approached Tanner, who was in the process of reaching up to grab another light fixture.

"I'm fixing the lights."

"Yeah, but ... what?"

It was in moments like these that Jason felt like an exacting mother. An intractable pragmatist, Jason was often aware that others perceived in him this unwanted impression of maternal comportment and secretly disparaged his rock n' roll reputation because of it. He did not want to be seen as the voice of reason not just because this gave the appearance of his being uninteresting but also because it was entirely inaccurate. He may be the first to pick up the slack where the other members of Lucky Boys Confusion and its road crew prove themselves unwilling or unable to practice better judgment, but it was the insidious boyhood delinquency lurking just behind Jason's prudent façade that made him more restless and perhaps more reckless than any of the others.

"Look!" Tanner said, grabbing another of the hallway light fixtures at its base, excited to demonstrate for Jason. "They bend down!"

Standing on the tips of his toes, Tanner slowly bent the candelabra downward.

"I can see that," Jason said.

"Adam showed me this earlier," Tanner confessed. "I'm almost done with the entire floor."

Jason looked behind Tanner and nodded.

"This is the sort of accomplishment that deserves a drink," he said, handing Tanner a plastic Gatorade bottle of red punch and vodka.

Tanner drank, his small stature instantly energized with confidence, and proceeded to complete his masterpiece.

It was a little after eleven.

There was an unspoken consensus in the lobby that the newly-arrived interloper, this swaggering, loping, drug-addled warhead of dissolute culture, was the certain cause of their present discomfort.

No one moved, and no effort was made to find even a single match in response to Adam's query. Even before a firing squad, I thought, they allow a man a final smoke.

Struck with an inspiration that must surely have been the result of those earlier drinks, I shouted, "Here you are, sir!"

Raising my hand above my head I made my way through the crowd, stepping on three feet, hard, as I approached Adam. I stood before him and produced a pack of matches with the hotel emblem emblazoned upon the cover. "They've got them in a dish over by the counter," I said, striking one and holding it up to the end of the cigarette sticking out of Adam's mouth. "But they're kind of hard to see behind this crowd."

Adam thanked me, demonstrating by his courtesy that he understood the direction of my histrionics. My appearance, less my earrings, was often mundane enough to pass for a private citizen when juxtaposed with the more eccentric rock star fashions of my friends. This night I was fortunate enough to be wearing a grey collared shirt and dark blue designer jeans that I had packed for some occasional relief from the dirty and stained denim used for rides between cities. I looked, then, less like the weathered roustabout I was than a young man traveling on business, my shaved head perhaps betokening premature balding and another mark of a maturity that further distanced me from Adam's rock star glam.

But our charade would only be viable for a few minutes before even the most tired and uneducated among those gathered saw through our silly game. But until that happened, I thought, we might have some fun with their confidence, and so I pretended to be a stranger to Adam and he pretended that I was a stranger to him in some strange impromptu Vaudevillian act.

"What's going on here? Who are all these people?" Adam asked. "I specifically requested that management keep my identity a secret."

"I'm afraid they're not here for you," I said. "Apparently there's been a fire or something. Didn't you see the fire trucks?"

Adam looked back over his shoulder to the flashing lights that flooded intermittently across his face.

"Oh. Those," he said, large plumes of smoke billowing out through his lips between words. "Yeah, I saw them."

"There seems to have been some bit of chicanery on the fifth floor tonight," I said. "Same old story, I'm afraid."

Adam shook his head. "The fifth, huh? That doesn't surprise me."

"You know, I was just saying the same thing," I said.

In a very short time the sour mood in the room had became almost unbearable, not the least because Adam was casting thick clouds of cigarette smoke into a smoke-free environment around a dozen or so young children. These children, I noticed, seemed to regard Adam as a sentinel from their approaching adolescence. Their eyes were wide with reverence, witnessing a hero in their midst. It didn't take long for their parents to accost him in the interest of protecting their young.

"Why don't you take that goddamned cigarette outside!" an especially indignant father shouted. I thought I recognized his voice.

Adam flicked some ash onto the carpet and considered this suggestion.

"I'm not sure that's a good idea," he said. "I'm not sure if you've noticed, but there seems to have been some sort of fire code transgression here tonight. And it might not be such a good idea to smoke around all those idling engines and leaking oil." He looked again over his shoulder and into the flashing lights. "I don't want to get a ticket."

"Then why don't you just get the hell out of here!" the man shouted.

"Aw, hell!" came another voice. "It was probably you and your fuck-up friends who started the fire anyway!"

"Fire?" Adam said. He looked questioningly at me before turning to address the crowd again. "Are you kidding? Where's the panic? Why aren't you all *outside* if there's a fucking fire *inside*?"

There was a noticeable lack of response to this question. Adam then continued. "No, it's probably something far more common. Probably some chick left her curling iron plugged in and laid it on her shoulder pads or something. Started smoldering and set off the fire alarm. I've seen this before, at least from fifth floor occupants."

I nodded. "Those shoulder pads are so that women can mimic the appearance of men."

Adam surveyed the crowd, squinting. "I'm not sure that these need any extra help."

"Why don't you two just leave!" someone shouted. "You're not welcome here!"

"Tough crowd," Adam muttered. "Apparently this Holiday Inn discriminates."

"Hey," I said, turning to Adam. "That reminds me of a joke. Why do Mary Kay saleswomen walk crooked?"

"Put out that goddamned cigarette!"

"I don't know," Adam said. "Why *do* Mary Kay saleswomen walk crooked?"

"You two are pathetic!"

"Get out of here!"

"Go home!"

"Their lipstick."

"Where are the cops?"

"What did he say?"

"If they started the fire, let's keep them here until the police come back down!"

Adam became incensed.

"What *fire*?" he demanded, stamping his foot. "You know, you cry wolf too many times and no one will believe you when you tell them that your daughter's dating a black man."

That was when the mob surged forward, their talons searching for flesh, craving retribution, blood, our tongues. We turned and leaped into the spinning door, and I was immediately afraid of becoming ensnared in a glass tomb as it became clogged with bodies eager for our meat, clutching and clawing against the glass. Using our combined weight we were able to shoulder the glass and metal forward, and we emerged into the cool night air, Adam's cigarette still smoldering.

I watched them pour against the glass, vitriol dripping from their lips, canines bared, eyes drawn into razor-like slits seething with confused arousal, their tempers stirred into lust and contempt.

But they were inside, and we were out, and we turned away in search of some solace, leaving them to their own devices.

Adam's phone rang.

It stopped, rang again, then stopped. The third time he answered, and I heard Tanner's voice, muffled but audible on the other end.

"Dude, is everything cool?" Tanner asked.

"Well," Adam began, seemingly on the cusp of telling Tanner the truth. He quickly reconsidered and said, "Yes. You should go back."

We were sitting on a bench in a public park where we seemed innocuous enough to pass under the gaze of passing police officers who might take offense to our presence at that time of night. The sound of running water from the fountain before us was soothing, the lights from inside the pool casting pleasant shadows against the night sky.

It was anyone's guess how long our fortunate solace would last. More accurately it was anyone's guess how long it would be before one of us decided to pee into the fountain.

"What happened?" Tanner asked.

"Nothing," Adam said. "You overreact."

"Are you at the hotel?"

"No."

"Why not?"

"Because."

There was a pause as Tanner processed Adam's responses.

"Are the fire trucks still there?" Tanner asked.

"No."

"The police?"

"No."

Pause.

"Then why the fuck don't you go back to the hotel?" Tanner demanded.

"We're just enjoying a beer in the park," Adam said.

"In the park? Why?"

"Because we're bored. Go back to the hotel and we'll be there in a little bit."

I felt a pang of remorse for Jason.

"Dude, you guys are pussies! If there're no cops, then it's cool!"

"Just let us know," Adam said, closing his phone.

"This is your way of getting back at Tanner, isn't it?" I said.

"I don't know what I'd be getting back at him for. He's just fun to abuse."

"And Jason?"

"He'll be fine. He'll understand."

I leaned back in my seat and became lost in the meditative rush of water as Adam handed me a beer.

*   *   *

Down the street Ryan approached the counter of a 24 hour convenience store, the blonde at his side, and slammed onto the counter a bottle of Skoal vodka, a box of condoms and a set of bungee cords. Looking the cashier in the eye, he said, "I'll be paying with food stamps."

"Then those girls over there are," I said.

"Them?" Adam said. "They're not hookers. They bought us drinks after the show."

"Well, let's bring them back to the hotel and get one of them to molest Tanner," I said.

The girls stumbled toward us, fighting against their heels.

They giggled, clinging to each other in solidarity as they noticed us.

They were both dressed in Dorothy ruby-red heels, Nantucket fishnet stockings, dandelion yellow miniskirts, halter-top plain white-T's sheltering prominent miracle-bra breasts and capped with faces like Van Gogh paintings, heavy with a thick coating of oily cosmetics.

Leaning into Adam, I advised, "Let's go for the shorter one for Tanner. She looks a little better."

"Hello," Adam said, smiling up at the girls.

They looked at us, shouldering their purses, taking inventory. They then laughed again, and the shorter, black-haired one said, "Oh! Hey! It's Lucky Boys!"

"Just one," I said. "I'm an unaffiliated sycophant."

"Would you like a beer?" Adam asked.

Their eyes glistened.

"Where's Tanner?" Adam demanded when we came upon Stubhy loitering on his phone in the now vacant hotel lobby.

"He's hiding. I think he's been traumatized," Stubhy said.

"We've got something to cheer him up," Adam said.

Stubhy looked past Adam to the two girls, the lighting wreaking havoc upon their appearance.

112

"Let's get them into the dark," he said. "Tanner's with Jason in their room."

"Where's Ryan?"

"Nobody's seen him since we checked in," Stubhy said, smiling at the girls. "Hi," he said to the first one, who melted with appreciation.

Something caught my eye as we stepped into the elevator. Looking down I asked, "Are those blood stains on the carpet?"

Most of the bottles in the room were still full. I stood with Stubhy and Katie, the brunette, near the doorway while at the other end of the room, Adam introduced Tanner and Jason to Samantha. Tanner sat in a cheap armchair, smoking a cigarette to calm his rattled nerves.

As Stubhy and I spoke with Katie, she wasted no time disclosing to us the unusual intricacies of her character.

"I spend most of my life hungry," she began from nowhere. "I don't like to eat. But then, I hate myself."

Stubhy and I said nothing.

"But it's not a defense, like the doctors will tell you," she continued.

"And what do medical professionals know, anyway," I said.

"And I don't say that to deceive myself, either. Most deceptions are a defense against hurting someone you love, and like I said ..."

"You ..."

"Yes."

"I see."

"Well that seems like all the time we have for unsolicited confessions today," Stubhy said, getting ready to pass to the other end of the room and a better conversation. But Katie continued, and he stayed.

"So as you've probably guessed, I'm Catholic," she said. "Eight siblings all vying for the same unrequited attentions. But, you know, father seldom answers us."

"That's got nothing to do with being Catholic," I said. "You shouldn't—"

"No," she said, cutting me off, "but it has everything to do with being a girl in my father's home and growing up in Wisconsin," she said.

"Meaning what?" Stubhy asked.

"Meaning that I could do whatever I wanted to because no one noticed. And holy shit, did I do whatever I wanted to. I still do."

Katie shifted, fidgeting with her beer and taking a deep drink. Then Katie brightened again.

"I was abducted by aliens!" she exclaimed.

Stubhy raised an astonished eyebrow, and Katie finished the last half of her beer. I handed her a fresh, uncapped bottle and urged her to continue.

"When I was twelve. Well, that was the last time. I was actually abducted a bunch of times since I was six. That's usually how they do it, you know. They find a good specimen and then they do repeated experiments on them."

There was a sudden and loud slamming against the door. The force of the weight crashing into it jarred the security chain hanging from the jamb and shook the 'privacy please' sign hanging from the handle. This startled Katie enough to provoke a small, surprised squeal that sounded like that of a frightened child. From the hallway we heard a muffled groan. Stubhy opened the door, and Toadie stood nursing his right shoulder, grimacing. He was wearing a shower cap.

"Goddamn," he said. "I thought the door was open, and I thought I'd make a dramatic entrance. But fuck, why'd you close it?"

Defeated, Toadie came in, passing Katie and offering her a meager hello. He went to sit on the edge of the bed near Jason and the others, still nursing his shoulder.

"Wow," Stubhy said after he'd passed. "So I don't remember what we were talking about. Seems like a perfect opportunity to change the subject."

"So how did these aliens kidnap you?" I asked, smiling at Stubhy's annoyance.

Katie, still a little unnerved by Toadie's arrival, said, "Well, I'd be asleep in my room at home, and you know, I'd suddenly have this awareness of someone, or some*thing*, in my room, in the dark. They'd be standing by my bed, just standing there not saying anything, just breathing really heavily."

"What did they look like?" I asked. Despite himself, I could see that Stubhy was becoming interested.

"Oh, they were human looking, definitely human looking. They'd have these big, enormous black eyes that you could see in the dark and really thin bodies. I wouldn't know what sex they were, and I wouldn't be able to move or scream or anything. They'd come toward me, breathing really heavily and reaching for me with these long fingers, and then I would just sort of black out."

"You'd black out?" Stubhy said.

"Yeah. But in the morning I'd kind of remember stuff, real hazy, like things they did to me. But it was weird, because time would almost stop. Like I would be moving really slowly, but they would be moving fast. They'd talk, but I couldn't understand what they were saying because it was too fast. Their voices were really deep."

"What kinds of things would they do?" Stubhy asked, adding, "Were they sexy aliens?"

"What? No! No," Katie said, giggling. "No, but they'd do, like, doctor stuff. They were checking to see if I'd be a good carrier, I think."

"A carrier?"

I handed Katie another fresh beer.

"Like for their kind. Or they were just doing experiments, trying to figure out human anatomy. I've read a lot about this. There are lots of people who've gone through the same thing," she said, becoming excited.

"Are they all from Wisconsin?" Stubhy asked.

"No! They're from all over! They're doing experiments on us all over the country and all over the world! They really are! There are lots of cases that we don't even know about because people are afraid to talk about it, because they're afraid that people will think that we're crazy!"

Stubhy looked at me and blinked several times in rapid succession, his mouth slightly agape.

Turning back to her, he asked, "Do you think they're coming back?"

"Well," she said. "They found me all those times before. Oh, and I don't trust people, for the most part," she added. "People only pretend to like you when they want something from you."

Katie drank. Then, perceiving that she was losing her audience as Stubhy and I both looked toward the other end of the room, curious to see what story Tanner might be telling and how it might compare to the one we'd just heard, she changed the subject.

"Like I was always very sexual, from a really early age. It was always something I was very open and comfortable with."

And so our interest in Katie was renewed, and we each uncapped another beer.

Across the room Katie's friend Samantha was feeding Tanner with attention while Adam, Jason and Toadie listened.

Samantha sat on the arm of the chair in which Tanner reclined. She leaned over him, one arm slung around his shoulder with the air of a saloon harlot lavishing accolades upon a potential customer.

Jason was sprawled upon the bed, his back against the wall, his legs splayed out before him, and Toadie sat cross legged at the foot of the bed. Adam stood, smoking and leaning against the long, waist high dresser. One arm rested on the silent TV.

Samantha, unfamiliar with Tanner's moods, asked, "Why are you so upset?"

"Because this fucker set me up!" Tanner shouted, gesturing toward Adam.

"He set you up?" she asked. "What do you mean?"

"Jason doesn't seem half as upset as you," Adam said.

"That's because Jason was parking the van while *I* walked up to the hotel *alone!*" Tanner said.

"So?" Samantha said. "What happened that was so terrible?"

Tanner took a deep breath.

"What happened is this," he said. "I walked up to the lobby, right? I figured that since Adam said everything was cool and the cops were gone and all I saw out front was one fire truck, I should have no problem getting back to our room. But when I got close enough to see inside, I saw that everyone was still crowded in the lobby. Now I'm feeling a little unsure, but I can't really turn around now, because I think that'd look suspicious. But I also think to myself that there's no way they can possibly know who did it, so I walk up to the doors—"

"Did what?" Samantha asked.

"Did?" Tanner said. "Nothing."

"We didn't tell them anything," Adam said. "We only told a couple of jokes."

"Well you told them *something*!" Tanner shouted. "When I walked in they all turned on me like *I* was the one who set the place on fire!"

"Set the place on *fire*?" Samantha said.

"Well, not really," Tanner said, squirming uncomfortably in his chair.

"By which he means not on purpose," Jason said.

"*Did* you set the place on fire?" Samantha asked.

Tanner studied her a moment before bellowing, "No! I didn't set anything on fire!"

"But you *did* make it so that the fire department and the cops had to show up," Jason said.

"How was I supposed to know that those shitty fucking lamps were going to start to burn the wallpaper?" Tanner said. "It's the hotel's fault for having cheap lamps like that so close to flammable surfaces."

"Oh, yeah," Jason said. "It's their fault they didn't take into account diminutive rock n' roll kids reconfiguring the lighting so that the heat from the bulbs would rise into the wiring, starting them smoking and possibly igniting an electrical fire."

"Is that what it was?" Tanner asked. "I thought it was the wallpaper."

"So you *did* cause the fire," Samantha said.

"So Tanner walked into the lobby," Adam interjected, quick to perceive a needless digression. "Then what happened?"

"Okay, so *then* I tripped in the revolving door as I was coming in, right? And when I did my wallet chains crashed into the glass and now *everyone* turned to look at me."

Adam shook his head. "The same fucking thing happened to me. See, you just rekindled their memory of me. That wasn't good."

"So I came into the lobby, and I must have looked responsible or guilty or something because they're all giving me the stink eye, but no one said anything. I asked somebody what was going on, why was everyone in the lobby, and then the mood really turned nasty and someone shouted, 'Why don't *you* tell *us*!'"

"Yeah, that was probably *partly* because of us," Adam said.

"I didn't know what the fuck to say. I just stood there, looking at all of these people. I tried to act innocent, but it came out real defensive, because I said 'What's *your* fucking problem?'"

"You always know the right thing to say," Jason said.

"So everyone got pissed off at me for that, and then I heard the elevator chime and hotel management and the chick from check-in came around the corner with the firemen. Now I started to get really freaked out. These people looked crazy! They looked like they wanted to pounce on me and tear my eyes out or something!"

"Are you always this dramatic?" Samantha asked, stroking Tanner's head.

"I'm serious!" Tanner shouted.

"Actually," Adam said, "just this once, I'd have to agree with Tanner."

"But he *is* always this dramatic," Jason added.

"Whatever—fuck you guys. So anyway, management came around the corner and told people that they could go back to their rooms. They said it was some sort of minor electrical thing on the fifth floor. Then someone in the crowd said that someone turned all of the lamps upside-down on the fifth floor, and now I started to inch backward toward the door. The fire chief said that, yes, someone did turn the lamps upside-down, probably thinking that it was harmless, but that it caused the fire alarms to go off and some of the sprinkler systems to activate."

"If you had just played it cool, you probably would've made out okay," Adam said. "How were they going to pin that on you?"

"But then the fireman has to add—and I mean who knows why he just *had* to add *this* little bit of information—that someone had also written the letters 'L B C' in red lipstick on the mirror in the hallway."

Jason laughed. "Oops." Adding slowly, "That was me."

"What?" Tanner erupted. "Where the fuck did you get lipstick?"

"Cincinnati, I think. I stole it from Lindsey."

"So technically, this is all Lindsey's fault," Adam said.

"I knew she was nothing but trouble," Toadie said, rolling a joint.

"So then I realized that I'm wearing a t-shirt that says what? 'Lucky Boys Confusion,' with the letters LBC emphasized in large block letters. But I have on my hoodie, and so I slowly started to zipper it up to cover up the t-shirt when I realized that 'LBC' is printed in huge letters across the back of the hoodie! I was still at the edge of the crowd because I had just come in, so I told myself that I might be okay if I can just keep my back from them. But then I started freaking out again because I thought that someone might see the reflection of the back of my hoodie in the glass behind me.

"All I could do was stand there, and then this guy, some huge ex-football player type, said, 'That stands for Long Beach California!' like he's some fucking genius for figuring that out. Then he turned to me, and because I must look like a California kid in his eyes, he said, 'I bet *you're* from California, ain't ya?' So now I just know that I'm fucked, and I was thinking, for the first time ever, that I wanted the cops to be there because these people were going to fucking hospitalize me."

"That's probably true," Adam said. "They were pissed that we'd gotten away earlier. They had a taste for blood."

"Dude, you guys make it seem like these people were all out of their minds on acid or something," Jason said.

"*You* never saw them!" Tanner shouted. "You were out parking the van the whole time!"

"True," Jason conceded. "Plus I stopped to smoke a jay, too."

"And it wasn't necessarily acid," Adam said. "They might just as easily have been beaked up on crystal meth or PCP."

"So this guy walked up to me, and he just *towers* over me. He's like seven feet tall or something, and I told him that I'm from Chicago. Of course he doesn't believe me, and the rest of the crowd was just sort of waiting to see what's going to happen. So I pulled out my wallet, and I had to open it really quickly because 'LBC' is scrawled across the front of *that*, too, and I pulled out my driver's license.

"He looked at my license, and when he saw that it's from Illinois, he kept looking at me, trying to find some way to prove that I did it. So he asked me what floor I'm staying on. I told him I'm on the tenth, and thinking fast, I show him my room key which has the room number written in black Sharpie across the back in case I forget. This finally seemed to satisfy the asshole, but he was still pissed that he couldn't prove anything. But now people have started walking away, heading back to their rooms, and he grunted and sort of shrugged and walked away. He said that if he finds out that it was me or one of my friends he's going to make us wish we never left California."

"It's lucky the guys from The Matches didn't stay here tonight," Jason said. "The plates on their van are from California."

"So everyone makes their way back to their rooms, and what did you do?" Adam asked, wanting closure.

"I just stood there. I didn't want to move because of the back of my hoodie and because I'd just seen my life flash before my eyes!"

"Yeah, I came in probably ten minutes later, and the lobby was completely empty," Jason said. "Tanner was still standing next to the door. He said that he'd almost gotten his ass kicked, but I thought he was just being Tanner."

"You just *had* to write LBC on the mirror, didn't you?" Tanner asked.

"I guess in retrospect I should've written 'bitch.' Or 'Tanner the merch vendor' for short."

"Regardless," Adam said, "we should probably keep a low profile for the rest of the night."

"Or just fuck everything up and pin it on me," Tanner muttered.

"That's not a bad idea," Adam said, hearing him. "And it seems to work so often in our favor."

While Tanner recounted near death experiences, Ryan and the blonde consumed vodka and each other in the back of The Lucky Van.

Katie was intoxicated, and she began making passes at anyone whose eyes happened to fall upon her as they tried to avoid her.

As Katie became more animated, her friend Samantha elapsed into a dissociative fugue.

"I took too many Seconals," she said.

"Seconals?" Tanner asked.

"And Vicodin."

"Vicodin?"

"And Xanax," she said, giggling as she spilled over onto Tanner.

The beer in her hand, still her first, was only half empty.

At one point while Katie was in the bathroom, Stubhy asked me whether I believed her story.

"I was into that stuff as a kid, but when I got older I stopped believing it. Then I saw a UFO one night while backpacking in Colorado."

"So you believe it?"

"Where there's smoke, there's fire, but most are manmade. Did you ever see the *Twin Peaks* movie?"

Katie returned.

"What're you talking about?" she asked.

"Brittany Spears," I said.

"Oh," she said, teetering. "She's nuts."

"I like to cut myself," Samantha said during a lull in the conversation.

"What? Why?" Tanner asked.

Samantha smiled and looked down at her arms, now shielded against the air-conditioning by a thin black pullover.

"I don't know," she said. "It feels good. It's ritualistic, like a lot of cultures do it. Ours is just too polished, too suburban-perfect and protective to really understand."

"You shouldn't do that," Tanner said, genuine concern in his voice.

Samantha seemed to relish his reaction.

"Tanner wants to put a cigarette out on your arm," Toadie said. "How about it?"

Samantha smiled, cocking her head to one side in consideration.

"Hell no!" Tanner shouted. "I'm not going to do that!"

Toadie offered in Tanner's stead, and when Samantha agreed, he said, "I don't smoke," and left.

Adam and I left Tanner and the others and ventured down to the lobby for inspiration but found no sign of Ryan. At the front desk Adam inquired about more matches and requested a wake-up call for November third, but the woman standing behind the counter didn't laugh.

With a fresh pack of matches in hand we walked toward the elevators. Along the way we caught sight of the bell hop's luggage cart standing empty and alone.

When we returned to room 1008, Adam was seated cross-legged upon a chair inside the luggage cart, his arms extended, his eyes concealed behind sunglasses. After several more cocktails and draws from the bottles at our disposal, Adam became convinced that the lampshades in the room would make excellent appurtenances for Katie and Samantha, and he insisted that we cut out holes for eyes and place them upon the girls' heads.

Next the girls were on the cart, and Adam and I pushed their cries of laughter down the long corridors of the hotel. There should have been angry protests and hotel security at our heels as we ventured from floor to floor, spilling beer and whiskey like breadcrumbs to map our progress, but our revelry was undeterred. No one accosted us, even in light of the night's earlier disturbances, proving that Adam's rock n' roll immunity was still sufficiently intact.

And on every floor, while we waited for the elevator, Adam lifted the receiver of the courtesy phone that automatically connected to the front desk and shouted, "This is Adam fucking Krier!" before hanging up without waiting for a response. When Adam picked up the phone on the sixth floor, a voice said, "Is this Adam fucking Krier?" to which Adam replied, "Who the fuck is that?"

By the time the doors opened on the fifth floor, we were prepared to retire, and that was when we came upon Ryan smashing lights with an empty bottle of vodka.

When we stepped back into the elevator, Ryan inspected the two girls huddled against each other upon the luggage cart and started to laugh. It's possible that Katie and Samantha, in their state of intoxication, had forgotten about the lampshades that hung about their heads like gumdrop halos, but it was just as likely that they were frightened into silence by Ryan's mania as he towered over them.

The blonde, meanwhile, stared.

"So who're you two supposed to be?" Ryan asked.

Her voice now incredibly languid, the syllables coarse and brittle, the first answered, "Samantha."

"Katie," said the second, her voice quiet and withdrawn.

"Adam thought they needed lampshades to shield their appearance from the light," I said. Turning back to the girls I asked, "Do you know the song Paper Moon?"

"Are they drunk?" Ryan asked.

Adam looked disgustedly at Ryan. "They're sitting on a luggage cart in a crowded hotel elevator at four in the morning with lampshades on their heads! What the fuck do you think?"

Ryan cocked his head in consideration. "I don't know. I'm not too familiar with Florida."

"Well, if you're not sure then perhaps you'd like to put the one who claims to have been abducted by aliens at the helm of a fully loaded 747 or the one who cuts herself at the controls of a nuclear reactor. Are they drunk? What's wrong with you, man? They—"

Adam stumbled and spilled a portion of his opened beer, managing to miss both Samantha and Katie but dousing the already fetid carpeting inside the elevator.

"Oh, shit," he said, holding up the bottle. "This is my last beer."

The elevator approached the tenth floor and passed it, ascending toward the fourteenth.

"Do those lampshades really shield you from the light?" Ryan asked. The girls looked up at him, the one quivering. "Do they make it easier to see?"

They said nothing.

The elevator stopped at the top floor, and there was a curious grinding of gears that seemed to come from the doors, which remained shut.

"Looks like we're stuck," Ryan said, pounding on the doors with one hand and tapping the alarm bell with the other. "No way out! Oh my God! Oh my *God*! No way out! No way *out*!"

It was then that Katie began to cry. Meek at first, the silence that fell upon the rest of the car in response to her misery only increased her anxiety, and soon she was sobbing, cowering into the corner and hugging her legs, the edge of the lampshade resting upon her knees.

At the same time there arose a solemn, cynical laughter that echoed behind the other paper lampshade. The laugh was dark and cryptic, like that of a sociopath witnessing the pleading of a victim before the fall of the axe. This was Samantha, lost in a tidal wave of opiate intoxication.

Their strange song became the only sound in the elevator, and as their discordant harmony grew, Adam retrieved the black Sharpie forever nestled in his pocket. He leaned over and drew upon the one lampshade a smiling mouth with raised eyebrows, and upon the other he sketched an exaggerated frown with a single tear falling from one eye.

He stepped back from his labor and said, "There. Now we know who you are."

We all regarded Adam's work, and we each became aware, in our own time, of Adam's mistake. For it was laughing Samantha who sat with the tearful eyes of tragedy, while Katie convulsed beneath the smiling mask of comedy.

As Adam was about to say something, the elevator came alive again and descended toward the lobby. When we reached the lobby, the doors opened upon an intoxicated middle-aged couple returning late after having missed the evening's prior disturbances.

They stepped back at the sight of us, and Adam shoved the luggage cart into the lobby, casting the two girls out to sea, saying, "Thanks again for coming!"

The blonde looked falteringly up at the couple, who watched the cart roll to a gentle stop on the carpet.

"Come on in," Ryan said, raising his bottle. "There's plenty of room."

The couple, too inebriated to act in good judgment, entered. The doors slid shut, silencing the sound of sobbing laughter.

"What floor?" Adam asked.

"Five, please."

The elevator started up, and I could taste a bilious resin in the back of my throat, ourselves trapped, the tension rising.

Growing Out Of It

On any given night of a Lucky Boys Confusion tour, each of the band members signs an endless number of autographs, scrawling their name across ticket stubs, CDs, flyers, arms, chests, backs—any available surface the fans request.

They descend from the stage and become accessible, smiling for photographs and many teenage fans' bragging rights at school. They graciously receive the accolades from sometimes shy and sometimes exuberant fans gushing with praise and admiration, and they attentively listen to fans' stories of their favorite LBC song and its particular importance to them.

To a longtime observer, these fans represent an ever-expanding spectrum of ages that is indicative of Lucky Boys Confusion's constant appeal to new crops of young fans despite their own increasing distance from high school and teenage adolescence. Somehow they have forged a special relationship with young fans that grow up to become the older fans whose steadfast devotion to Lucky Boys Confusion sustains the size and enthusiasm of their crowds.

Key to their continued appeal is their consistently frenzied stage performance. Lucky Boys Confusion has never forgotten that for their fans, any particular night may be their first or last memory of the band. They have hearts to win and a reputation to prove, and so they have never succumbed to the rock n' roll pitfall of taking their fans' enthusiasm and approval for granted.

"A lot of our support comes from seeing our live show," Stubhy said, eating bar food in a cramped booth on the road. "I think that's how we tend to win most of our fans, and that's why we put so much emphasis on touring. Our live show is where you really get a feel for our style and our music. Recording an album in a studio, for instance, is an entirely different musical performance. In the studio it's never simply about playing the song together and getting it right. You have all kinds of unique and interesting effects that allow you to be creative, but they don't always translate into a live performance. There are some bands that excel in the studio but don't do so well onstage. I could name a few. Personally, I'd rather command the stage, and I'm glad that we've always put that first. If a song doesn't work onstage, if it doesn't interest the crowd and get them moving, then it's probably not going to interest them on a CD either. That's always been our approach since we started writing music and playing in people's basements."

Stubhy, Joe, Adam, Jason, Ryan 1999

Part of the attraction of any teenager's music choice, apart from its occasional capacity to shock their parents, is its ability to emote a shared experience and stimulate the common empathies of youth searching for identity and belonging. It is an escape from the pressures and dictums of their parents and schoolteachers, a voice at once speaking and listening, both delivery and reception, and when looking for Lucky Boys Confusion's particular appeal, this seems to be the marrow about which every other aspect is structured.

"That observation about our fanbase remaining so consistently young—that's the reason to do it, the motivation to keep writing music," Adam said, lounging backstage before a show in Columbia, Missouri. "Think about when you and I were in high school and how important music was to us. We'd find a song or a band we liked and play it over and over again at parties or driving around in somebody's car. Certain lyrics said all of the things that we were feeling or all of the things that we wanted to say. It was like, 'yeah, that's it exactly, they just said it perfectly.' So when a kid tells us that our music really helped them or that some lyric we wrote encouraged them through a rough time, that's when it all makes sense. That's when you feel this incredible satisfaction that's hard to describe.

Adam, 2003 (photo Nabil Elderkin)

"I have a fascination with coming of age stories," Adam continued later. "It's the Holden Caulfield *Catcher in the Rye* thing. I love that time of life, that age and those cheesy movies like *Breakfast Club* and *Sixteen Candles*. I think I always identified with those stories, and I wanted to write songs that would express that same idea. I think I sort of wanted to return the favor because so many kids feel that sense of isolation and dejection. I like to think that we can be a place where kids can feel accepted or feel like they belong, even if it's only during that song or during that concert. That's so much of what rock n' roll always meant for me."

Searching for some way to sum up his idea, he said, "I like to think of us as coming of age set to music."

The band has reason to believe that this sentiment appeals to its fans. Lucky Boys Confusion's first national exposure was built upon the single "Fred Astaire." In the true spirit of Lucky Boys Confusion, the lyrics to "Fred Astaire" describe an adolescent suffocating under a parent's best intentions.

They're pushing these children,
for all the wrong reasons
So far, man you're crushing down their spirits.
Suffocate, emancipate, turn their backs
and walk away

"I wrote those lyrics primarily for my mother," Stubhy said. "When I was young she was really domineering. She tried to push me into all of these activities that I didn't want to do. I just wanted to breathe and be myself. I was a kid and I didn't know what I wanted to do, but I knew I didn't want to participate in all of these things my mother signed me up for. It was difficult because it also became this source of shame, too. I didn't want to disappoint her or hurt her feelings, but I was also unhappy that she wouldn't give me space to find interests of my own. Finally, I rebelled.

"Of course by that time I probably wanted to hurt her feelings. I know that she cared about me and wanted what was best for me, and I guess the other end of the spectrum is having parents who don't care at all. But that song was my way of telling

129

parents that they need to give their kids space, or eventually they'll turn their backs on everything, including their parents, and they won't know who they are or what they want to do."

The lyrics to "Rolling Rock," written while Adam was still in high school, express a similar theme of the teenager struggling with their burgeoning autonomy. In this song the speaker, clearly a teenager, arrives home late to find his parents angry and waiting, sparking loud arguments and the parents' threat of medication to quell what seems to be their child's erratic behavior.

> No one can stop me from being myself,
> I'm quite capable of that I can tell.
> I don't need your chemicals
> to make me feel the way you think I should.

"That song has all the emotion of a high schooler—coming home late and getting into a fight with their parents because they feel like they're losing control of their kid. And in a way they are losing control because in high school you start to grow up and move on," Adam said in another conversation. "I still like that song, and so do the fans, even if the lyrics are a bit too simple. It's a great sing-a-long."

Adam.

The lyrics to "Rolling Rock" are certainly straightforward enough and clearly demonstrate an adolescent hand, but there is something inviting in their simplicity, something that makes them accessible and almost universally relatable for today's teenager. And the medication, referred to pejoratively as 'chemicals,' becomes a metaphor for overbearing control and parental subjugation. This is a theme that recurs in many LBC songs because the two primary songwriters, Stubhy and Adam, share a strong interest in that age, and Stubhy especially understands that time as one of misanthropy, confusion and rebellion.

"He got picked on a lot when he was growing up," Adam said of his friend. "I mean a lot. He got shit from everybody, and I think that really fucked with him. He feels like he has to constantly prove himself, and he wants to be a part of everything."

Stubhy, full name Kaustubh, is a first generation Indian. His parents arrived to America from Maharashtra, a state in India populated with many poor villages where childhood was a struggle against oppressive poverty. In America his parents' approach to rearing their children involved isolating them from the pejorative influences of the strange culture into which they had come. Stubhy's parents elected to quarantine their three children from that culture in an attempt to preserve their children's Indian heritage and purity, thus preventing Stubhy and his siblings' socialization into a culture that was difficult enough for any adolescent to navigate, to say nothing of those whose parents were entirely alien to it. Stubhy's story, which can be extrapolated to apply to most adolescents' struggles against their parents, reveals how this insular atmosphere can stymie an adolescent's social and personal development while nurturing an ambitious personality in retaliation to that suffocation.

"My parents were a little harder, I think, than a lot of others. My father was a lot harder than most Indian parents, and I'm a little more rebellious than most Indian kids—at least in comparison those I knew growing up. First, there was this huge generational and cultural gap that. Combine that with my parents' overbearing approach to raising me and you've got a really incendiary environment, and it just exploded when I hit high school.

"When I was growing up, I wasn't allowed to listen to music or watch football or basketball—no sports at all, actually. I had to be in by five o'clock every day, and I wasn't allowed to keep any friends. I couldn't watch television except for the news, which my father made me watch every day, and I had to read and write in my father's native language for at least an hour every day. When I had homework from school, I'd have to come home and do Indian homework on top of my schoolwork and translate my schoolwork into my father's language. I look back at it now and I think that some of it was positive. It has helped me throughout my life. I mean, I'm fluent in three languages because of all of that, but some of it was just unnecessary and cumbersome. It was suffocating.

"At some point I started sneaking books on movies, TV, football, baseball—anything related to the popular culture that I'd been kept from. Back in grade school, when sports were the center of life for all the other kids, I would read every book I could about every sport that the other kids were interested in. I learned the players' statistics, and I learned the language and the concept of the games. I had no idea what a 'skip-on' was, I just knew that Walter Payton was the best at it because that's what it said in everything that I read. I could name every position and every player who played it and their statistics, but I couldn't visualize it in my head. They were just names and titles and numbers. But that's how I would try to fit in with other kids and interact with them.

"I knew about politics and economics at age ten. I was watching the news when most kids were watching *The Simpsons*. I didn't really know what *The Simpsons* were until high school. I mean, this was the time when everybody was walking around in those 'Underachiever,' and 'Don't have a cow, man' Bart Simpson t-shirts, and I remember going to the library and reading articles about the show and memorizing the characters. This way, when some kid in junior high tried to make fun of me by asking me about it, I could talk as though I'd seen it. Meanwhile I had no real idea of what it was or who the characters actually were.

"So there was this huge culture gap between myself and almost every other kid. The other Indian kids whose parents had assimilated into American culture had an easier time, but my dad refused to accept American culture. He just didn't really understand it or the struggles of growing up in it. My dad's a complex character. He's a certified genius. He placed second in the Bachelor of Engineering exams in India, and if you know anything about those exams and India, you know that's saying a lot. He came from a really poor part of India, and he didn't have any friends growing up, and so he didn't put a lot of emphasis on social interaction. He just didn't understand how that was important or how you couldn't have just five shirts and two pairs of pants and be happy, or how the kinds of clothes you wore and what kinds of activities you were into would get you friends.

"I mean, in one sense, that tells you about his values and how he didn't buy into American commercialism, but it also made me a real outsider. Kids just glom onto that one oddball, the one they think is weaker, and give him all kinds of shit so they can feel better about themselves. I got harassed, and I got my ass kicked on a regular, almost daily basis.

"But there's another reason that I got picked on more than some of the other kids. Even though I was the biggest nerd in school, I was also extremely cocky. Every kid could hate me, but I would still tell the biggest kid in school to go fuck himself. I was the one who would tell the kids who beat me up yesterday that they were fucking assholes today, which would only get me beat up some more.

"I knew that I was smarter than they were, and so in some ways I didn't really care what they did or what they said to me. That's one of the things that people misunderstand about me. They think I'm cocky because I'm in a band and I'm the frontman and I think I'm some big shot, but I've been this way since I was seven. I've always been that sort of reclusive asshole who's part defense and part arrogance."

Adam, Stubhy, Ryan.

Stubhy smiled and continued.

"There was this huge exposure that happened about the time that I got to high school, and my rebellion really started to kick in late into my sophomore year. I started getting bad grades, staying out late, hanging around bad kids and going to parties every night—I just didn't give a shit. Looking back on it, I think I was just blaming my parents for never having had any friends or a social life, and I wanted to rub my social life in their face.

"I started to get a glimpse of friendship and the power that came with being popular. I knew that I didn't want to do the school-thing by junior year, and I started writing poetry. Bands like Nirvana really started to affect me, and I fell in love with other bands from all different kinds of genres. It was all so new to me. I didn't have any idea that people typically confined themselves to one or two particular genres of music. I can remember thinking that the music to those old *Juicy Fruit* commercials was cool because it was sort of like rock n' roll, and I also thought the lyrics were loaded with sexual innuendoes. I also loved the Magnavox commercials, and it wasn't until I was twenty years old that I realized that the music in that commercial was The Beatles. I remember calling up Adam in the middle of the night to tell him, I was so excited. I think he hung-up on me because he couldn't care less. It was old news to him and everyone else.

"So when I finally broke out from under my parents' thumb, I just started listening to everything that I could get my hands on. Then one day one of my buddies was jamming with some other kids at a friend's house. He asked if I played any instruments, and I told him that I didn't, but I could sing. I'd been in choir in junior high, and I sometimes liked to sing my poetry. He'd invited me to their practice with no real interest, just as something to fill the time. At one point while the band was playing a song, I started to sing along to it. When the song was over they asked me what it was that I'd just sung. I told them it was something I'd just scribbled down, sort of off the top of my head, and I remember being aware that they didn't believe me. They let it go because I was their friend, but they really thought I'd stolen it from somewhere.

"There were people from these other bands at the house that day, and I remember feeling a sense of being rewarded for something that I'd taken for granted. That was the first time that it clicked, when I realized that I was pretty good at this and people thought I was good. A little while later I made friends with this weird kid who sat next to me in study hall, and we started playing music together. Eventually we formed the band Farmboy and started playing shows.

"My parents' reactions to my behavior during that time ran the gamut from anger, to hope, to disappointment. They tried everything to bring me back into the fold. Between my junior and senior year of high school they sent me to India to get me away from all of the trouble that I was getting into here in the states. That didn't really help, though, and I was a little pissed off because it took me away from my band all summer. All I did in India was discover beer and smoke a lot of weed.

"When I came back I gave my band a call to ask what was crackin', and they told me how throughout the summer people had been saying how much they liked Farmboy. They had been asking us to play shows all summer long. I remember thinking, 'Well, this must be it. This must be the reason that I was freaking out for the last two years.' Until then it had felt like I was getting bad grades and acting out for no reason, but I was just caught up in finding something. I'd tried to find what I was good at, and that turned out to be music.

"Farmboy won the battle of the bands at the Hinsdale Community Center in our senior year, and that's when you and Adam found us," he said, referring to the time when Adam and I, who used to go to local concerts every weekend in high school, first discovered the band Farmboy and subsequently Stubhy and Ryan.

"After graduation I went away to Eastern Illinois University, and Farmboy broke up. I was there for a semester, and when I came home Adam contacted me and we rode around in a van and wrote the song Back Then. Next he showed me the music to 40/80, and we wrote some words to it. We named our band Lucky Boys Confusion and played our first show in somebody's backyard in June, probably as part of a graduation party. At that point I decided to scrap school. I had decided that being in a band was what I wanted to do with my life."

Despite the particular extremes of his upbringing, Stubhy doesn't feel that the struggles he went through were much different from most other American teenagers.

"A lot of it is what anybody goes through growing up. I think that every kid feels that pressure to figure out answers to questions like, 'what's going to make me cool, what's going to make me stand out, what's going to make me not get picked on?' The subject matter of our music is close to that struggle of growing up, whether it's growing up between twenty-one and twenty-eight or thirteen and eighteen. It's all growing up, and there's a certain degree of angst that goes along with that."

In a private conversation later, Adam said, "He's twenty-eight and he's still going through the same things that kids go through when they're in high school, trying to figure out who they are and who they want to be. I think that's part of what keeps him in touch and relevant to our audience. Part of it might be that he's never satisfied. He's always reaching out and searching for new angles, new sounds and new interests, and that's a great personality to have in a band. It's not insecurity, I think he's just restless and a little tormented."

"In the end," Stubhy said, "you're getting your ass kicked by everybody, and if you start letting people take you down, you're never going to get anywhere. That's been my approach to life, and it's sort of had to become our approach as a band."

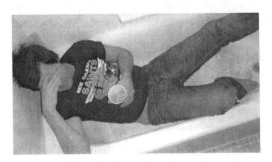

Ryan. Sullen.

Truck Stop en Route

It was still morning, and the sunlight was already harsh, pounding hot sandstorm air into our emaciated and cowering limbs. With each throbbing in our temples the heat would close in upon us, smothering the air from out of our struggling lungs. Our words were parsed, and we squinted against a million points of light stabbing us in the eye.

The scent of gasoline was thick, and we watched the ethanol vapors rising about us, the steaming exhales of metallic beasts turning the world into the memory of a macabre acid trip.

We each observed a nearby caravan of families pausing from their vacation road trip for gas, bathrooms and food. Their presence filled the air with shrieking tantrums and mirthful pleas for attention.

Someone mentioned going inside, and we crossed the blacktop to the sprawling convenience store thrumming with air-conditioned solace.

Once inside it quickly became apparent that the band was somewhat out of their element.

The night before, in a fit of First Amendment inspiration, Stubhy had written 'cunt' across the knuckles of his left hand with a Sharpie, while across his right he had written 'fuck.' Adam, meanwhile, had not given much thought to his densely matted hair after awaking on a deck chair beside the indoor swimming pool of last night's hotel. Unsure where he was or how he had arrived, much less how he had been allowed to pass the night there, he was soon accosted by squealing children who ran screaming past him to cannonball into the green waters, sprinkling him with small droplets of chlorine and urine. There were strange stains and stranger smells about his clothes, and the inside of his mouth still tasted like rancid bathwater.

Ryan teetered between collapsed exhaustion and irritable outbursts, and Joe's hair stood curiously up on its ends without the aid of any hair cosmetic. His own recollection of the night before ran like a silent film filled with gross inaccuracies and missing scenes.

Tanner's hair had met with a pair of electric clippers only hours before, and now his shock of blond hair, before a Mohawk, had a large patch missing near the crown of his head. There were also curious splashings of red and black dye about his hair from what had been left of Stubhy's hair dye, giving him the appearance of a dilapidated punk rock cheetah.

I was road weary and hungover, but my unremarkable shaved head and leather riding jacket made me far less conspicuous than my friends.

Stubhy approached the Subway sandwich counter. A mother standing nearby turned to see the approaching tawny fiend and drew her gaping child toward her.

Stubhy avoided her look.

The man behind the counter, rotund with drooping jowls, large beefy hands and red, irritated splotches of burst capillaries about his cheeks and forehead took Stubhy's order with a sanctimonious air of disapproval.

"A BLT," Stubhy said. "On wheat bread."

The man opened and slammed shut some oven doors.

"Cheese?" he asked.

"American."

The man's fingers struggled to separate the slices for him. He slapped the meat down on top of the cheese and tore away the tissue paper with the flair of a Bulgarian cosmetologist administering another Brazilian wax.

"Then what toppings would you like?"

He spat the word 'toppings' like a violent obscenity.

"All of them."

The man grunted, decrying Stubhy's gluttony.

"And mustard?" he asked, looking up, pushing the sandwich away from him as though it were an abomination.

"Yes."

He splashed mustard about the pile of meats, cheeses and vegetables and flung it aside. He then folded the bread and cut the finished product, seeming to envision the blade being drawn across the neck of a sacrificial lamb, and thereafter wrapped the decaying carcass in folds of fresh tissue paper.

He took Stubhy's money and handed him his change without looking at his face. When Stubhy reached out to retrieve his sandwich, the man noticed the large letters of his right hand glaring up at him. He stopped in the process of replacing the money into the cash till and looked up at Stubhy.

"Is that the latest fashion among you pretty boys nowadays?" he asked.

"Something like that," Stubhy said. "It's what I like to do. If you were going to write your hobby on your knuckles you'd have a hard time fitting 'beat my wife and fuck my daughter' on one hand, asshole."

The man's face turned an intense red, the red splotches spreading like melted butter about his sizeable cheeks and neck. As he struggled to find words, Stubhy turned and walked away, grabbing a cookie from the counter that he didn't intend to pay for.

"Get *out*! Get *out* you filthy ... filthy ... *Indian*!"

Stubhy raised a middle finger behind him as he stepped languidly through the glass doors, jingling a set of small brass bells that hung above.

The restaurant was still. The mother from before, seated in a booth with her son, turned a look of fear and loathing over her shoulder as Stubhy departed.

Hungry and having not yet ordered, I bit my lip and remained silent. After he had regained a modicum of composure, the man slammed the cash till closed and approached me at the far end of the counter.

Intending to mollify his blood pressure before it threatened to collapse his feeble heart, leaving me hungry and sandwich-less, I thought I would try to stroke his insecurity.

"Don't mind him," I said. "He's Jewish."

139

The man looked at me, suspicious.

"You think?"

I shrugged.

"Yeah," he said, looking in the direction Stubhy had gone. "You're probably right." He chortled and then grinned. "Goddamned Jew."

This seemed to please him, and he set about making my sandwich with satisfaction.

As I paid, he added, "Goddamned Jews, eh?"

"Yeah," I said. "You'd think that they'd suffered enough than to want to eat this shit."

Back outside the sun continued to spit venom upon us.

The band stood around the van, milling furtively about, trying to avoid the sun.

"I hate the South," Stubhy said, handing the absconded cookie to Jason.

"It's not all bad," I said. "This is the land of blues and the birth of rock n' roll, after all."

Stubhy sighed a begrudging assent.

"Anyway, fuck that guy," I said. "I keyed a Star of David into his car door."

I pointed across the parking lot to a car parked around the corner from the entrance. The dashboard was littered with Subway wrappers, and a confederate flag hung from the rearview mirror.

The band climbed back into the shade and air-conditioning of the Lucky Van, and I climbed onto my bike, eager for the blessing of the wind to wash away the morning's pain.

New Orleans

A beer bottle soared across the conference room, liberated and free for one beautiful, tranquil moment.

"Teenwolf!"

The bottle, empty, impacted with the wall. It bounced backward and plummeted to the floor with a soft thud.

"Hey, Teenwolf!"

For the past week Adam had been nicknamed 'Teenwolf' for the thick mane of hair that crowned his head like an irregular distended halo, unwieldy, untamed and unclean.

Adam turned in the direction of the call and spied a table near the rear of the room, behind a small sea of placid faces.

"Yeah, Teenwolf!" an older gentleman said, waving his hand above his head. His nose was red, his hair white, his features robust. "Come here and let us buy you a shot!"

The unfamiliar man sat beside his wife, and the two of them appeared old enough to be Adam's parents. Seated around them at the table were Ryan, Joe and myself. We'd made friends with them and had been enjoying his rounds of drinks.

"Your friend here was telling us that you're like a modern day Isaac Newton," the man said as Adam approached.

"The bottles don't break!" Adam exclaimed.

"They'll break eventually, I'll betcha! And if they don't break, then soon enough they'll break *you!*" the man said, seeming to find this clever.

"Take a seat, Teenwolf," Ryan said, smiling. "They're impressed."

"What's your pleasure?" the man asked.

"Black Sambuca," Adam said, sitting down.

"Black Sam—so *that's* it! Soon you'll be spending the night on the throne with the green shits, sure enough!" the man said, and he erupted into a loud spate of laughter, dousing us with another blast of sour whiskey vapors.

Adam picked up an empty bottle from our table and launched it across the room.

The man's wife, silent, looked displeased and a little frightened by her physical proximity to Adam's apparent dementia.

Earlier, as Adam sat at the bar, he had accidentally knocked a half-empty bottle of Bud Light to the floor. Impressed that the bottle had bounced, once, rather than shatter into pieces on the floor, Adam's reverence for reproducible and observable data had then prompted him to draw deeply from the beer in his hand and thereafter hold the empty bottle out before him, releasing his fingers as he swallowed.

The bottle fell, bounced and came to rest.

Adam then repeated the experiment and alerted Joe, who sat beside him, to his remarkable discovery.

"Watch this," he said, elbowing Joe.

For added effect, Adam raised his arm above his head and released the bottle into the ether.

Joe watched as the bottle, still intact, returned to the earth after bouncing once.

"Did you *see* that?" Adam asked.

"It's called carpeting, Adam."

"But this is a *bar*!" Adam exclaimed.

"It's a hotel conference room that they turned into a bar," Joe said.

"But they don't break! It's like fool-proofing a bar. Even if you wanted to, you couldn't break these bottles."

"I'm sure if you wanted to," Joe began, but he stopped himself before finishing. Adam tossed another bottle in front of them. The bottle hit the ground, bounced twice and came to rest.

"Look! It did it again!"

Joe rose from his stool and walked away.

Our makeshift bar, carpeted, was located in the Kennedy conference room of the New Orleans Wyndham Hotel, near the airport. Knowing better than to upset tourists and local Louisiana patrons with an egregious deficiency of drinking space while the hotel underwent extensive renovations, the resourceful management had turned the conference room into a temporary bar, removing most of the unnecessary furniture like podiums, microphones and other multi-media hardware. The result was a sparsely furnished room littered with a small multitude of folding tables and chairs and a long simple counter with several stools alongside it.

After Joe had left him for better company, Adam found that other patrons seated nearby were giving him a more satisfactory reception. This audience seemed impressed by his antics as he downed increasing amounts of beer to procure more bottles to cast into the air and entertained by the showmanship with which he executed this performance. By the time I entered and took a seat with Ryan and Joe and their new friends, Adam's experiments had devolved into throwing the bottles across the entirety of the room with an energy more sinister than that of innocent scientific inquiry. The menacing expression on his face coupled with the savage qualities of his physical appearance as he wound up like a pitcher at the mound, taking aim at the far wall, seemed to intimidate the Wyndham employees into silence. No one, not even the bartender, felt confident enough to confront him or to suspend his service.

Most remarkable, however, was how the evening crowd continued to talk complacently among themselves, seemingly unaware of or indifferent to the wild-haired menace throwing empty beer bottles nearby. Several people raised occasional cheers as they watched in awe of the young man's temerity, but Adam was more or less just another fixture in an otherwise ordinary New Orleans landscape.

"So why the name Teenwolf?" the man asked.

Adam didn't answer but instead threw another emptied bottle against the nearest wall. His arm seemed to have lost some of its control and accuracy, finally succumbing to the massive amounts of liquor coursing through it, and the bottle soared erratically through the air like a crippled pigeon before falling against the wall.

"I'll bet it's because of your crazy hair, eh?" the man continued.

"No," Adam said, turning back to him. "I got the name because I like to surf on top of vans, shave my back and drink the blood of unbaptized young. Like Whitney Houston in her prime."

The man erupted with another blast of sour whiskey air, and the cocktail waitress returned with our round.

"To Teenwolf," the man said. "And unbreakable bottles!"

And Teenwolf drank, the night still young.

The day had been spent on the road, and the compounding toll of constant travel had begun to deplete the excitement that fuels the initial departure from home. The van, before white, now takes on a darker hue, stained with the dirt and grime of endless miles of sun and rain and night-soaked pavement, scarred with new abrasions and new wounds.

As the novelty of the road is replaced by routine, a certain degree of enervation consumes the early vitality, and a period of repetition and exhausted patience replaces the first weeks of energized rebellion.

Tanner. Asleep in The Lucky Van.

"It's an interesting pattern," Stubhy said. "In the first two or three weeks, everyone is supercharged and ready to go. After that comes several weeks of this lull where we're tired and irritable. By the end of a tour, we manage to pull ourselves out of that, and we're back to the energy of the opening of the tour.

"We've done a lot of touring over the past four or five years, and so we're pretty familiar with that pattern. We can recognize when it's happening. Knowing what's going on doesn't make you any less susceptible to its influence, but at least we're more capable of managing it. The road, after all, has a way of destroying bands. It's stressful. It's a lot of fun, sure, and we're not pushing paper at a day job, but people tend to overlook the fact that it still has its own degree of stress.

Stubhy, Adam. On the road.

"I usually tell people to think of their four or five closest friends. You'd love to quit your job and travel the country in a van, playing music to crowds of adoring fans every night, making a little bit of money and having a good time. Who wouldn't? This

145

was our dream, and we're lucky as hell to be doing it for this long. But you also have to consider that in every place you go, you essentially only have each other. The fans are there, sure, but they get to stay. They go home, they go back to their own lives, and the next day you move on to the next city to do it all over again. It becomes hard to know where you fit in, and sometimes you begin to feel like you're just a supplement to other people's lives without one of your own.

"So then the question becomes, how well do you really know your friends? How long would you be able to handle being cooped-up in the same car with them hour after hour, day after day, and then share what's essentially the same hotel room night after night, week after week?

"You have to factor in exhaustion, of course, and then you have to consider everybody's personality and particular quirks. Then add alcohol and, depending who you are, drugs, and how long do you think you'd last? Look, we're not martyrs. We love this. But sometimes I think people have a romanticized notion of what this life is like that doesn't take into account some of its stresses, too. It's not for everybody. We've made it this long, and I think we'll be able to make it a lot longer, but ... there may be a limit."

Pounding.

"Hey!"

More pounding.

"Open this goddamned door!"

Following another succession of fierce pounding, the door opened, and Adam nearly fell atop of Joe, who stood in the doorway, bleary-eyed and irritated.

"Joe," Adam said, recovering his balance. "What the fuck are you guys doing?"

"We're sleeping. Go away."

"Sleeping? At this hour?"

"We're done. Go away." Joe pushed Adam into the hall and started to close the door.

Adam quickly righted himself and charged the door, trying to force himself between it and the jam before it closed. He succeeded in contacting only the metal partition before bouncing backward onto the floor. He struggled to his feet, approached the door and continued shouting, "Hey! You cock-eyed fecal-pheliac goat fuckers better answer this door!"

Silence.

Bored, Adam turned to a new victim across the hall and began drumming a beat upon the door. He soon became lost in the rhythm, his eyes closed, his head bobbing along the current of his beat, and just as he reached the climax of a dramatic flourish that incorporated a complex system of alternating knuckle-raps and bass-beating open-palm slams, the door opened and an older man stood facing him. He was short and mustached with thinning grey hair, and his eyes were heavy with sleep. A considerable paunch hung over the waistband of his plaid sleepwear, and Adam thought he smelled mint julep seeping out of his pores.

Surprised, Adam found nothing to say.

"Can I help you?" the man asked petulantly, his southern accent thick.

Adam groped for words. Finding some, he said, "Stubhy. You look awful. It's called Botox."

"Now you listen to me, you little *prick*," the man said, raising a menacing finger and pointing it at Adam's face. "If you so much as *bump* into this door again I swear by God I'll put you in the hospital you shit-faced cocksucker."

"So much for Southern hospitality," Adam said.

The door slammed in his face.

Adam sighed.

"I had bigger expectations for New Orleans," he said to the vacant hallway.

Stubhy's eyes glistened, a mischievous conflagration raging behind them.

"Where did you get that?" Jason asked.

"St. Louis."

"That makes sense."

"She's top of the line. She has three orifices."

147

"Oh yeah?" Jason said. He looked at the doll skeptically. "Three, huh?"

"Yeah. Three. Top of the line," Stubhy said.

"So that's top of the line, I guess," Jason said.

Stubhy met his look and became irritated. "What?"

"No, it's nothing. I mean, if that's top of the line, then I guess—"

"You guess that *what*? What the fuck is *wrong* with her?" Stubhy demanded, shaking the doll.

Jason shrugged. "It's nothing, really. It's just that if I were going to buy a doll like that, I'd probably want my money's worth, is all." Jason pursed his lips, scrutinizing the doll. "Just seems like kind of a rip-off."

"A rip-off?" Stubhy said, incensed.

"I'm just saying," Jason continued. "So long as it's a sex doll, why not give it a glass eye, you know, or an eye patch. It could have had an accident."

Stubhy looked incomprehensibly at his friend.

"What?" Jason said defensively. "You've never wondered?"

"I can't believe you're telling me you want to skull-fuck her."

Jason shrugged. "Not many people ever get the chance, is all. I mean, *I* don't want to do *any*thing to her. All I'm saying is that if a thing's worth doing, it's worth doing right, and if you're depraved enough to fuck a doll in the ass then you probably don't have too many scruples about fucking it in the eye either."

Stubhy probably didn't think that he could ever manage to look indignant while holding a naked, tri-orificed inflatable doll in the middle of a vacant 12 a.m. ninth floor hallway somewhere in New Orleans, but he somehow managed it.

"You are seriously fucked in the head, Jason," he said.

"No pun intended, I'm sure."

A door opened several rooms away from where they stood, and a late middle-aged woman emerged. She wore a heavy white bathrobe and carried an empty bucket for ice. Her faded yellow hair was disheveled, and without cosmetics she looked pale and tired. She closed the door behind her and was turning to walk the other way down the hall when she glanced in Stubhy and Jason's direction.

They looked at her, expressionless and silent, and she looked at them, her eyes darting from one to the next, resting the longest on the doll at Stubhy's side, considering its sinister implications. The doll itself only looked back at her with a permanent expression of shock stitched into its face.

The doll was blonde.

They stood in silence, and only once did Stubhy shift his arm slightly, the doll's plastic arm rubbing against its own plastic torso and making a momentary abrasive screech like a crow in labor.

Never taking her eyes from them, the woman reached into her bathrobe's pocket and withdrew her keycard. In a trance she slid it into the door handle and removed it. A muffled whirring and clicking of small gears sounded in the silence. Perhaps forgetting her intended errand or perhaps preferring the sanctity of her room at the expense of a cold drink, she looked away, turned the handle and stepped back across the threshold, leaving Jason and Stubhy undisturbed.

When the door had closed, Jason turned back to Stubhy and said, "So what are we going to do with her?"

"First, we're going to get her into a Lucky Boys t-shirt," Stubhy said. He turned and headed for the elevators.

"You got the key for the trailer?" Jason asked.

"Come on, Caligula. It's under control."

Adam loped back to his room, his shoulders slumped forward in discouragement, and violently kicked open the door. Venting his frustration, he entered the room in a mad flurry of animated footwork like some despondent and intoxicated Pinocchio stealing in upon Mister Geppetto to exact some overdue revenge.

Ryan sat cross-legged at the foot of the bed, topless, a bottle of whiskey between his legs and his eyes concentrated upon the TV as he scanned its channels with the remote control. He did not satisfy Adam's appeal for attention apart from asking,

"Do you think we could rent a porno and charge it to another room?"

"Fuck that," Adam said. "Where are the girls? Stubhy needs one."

"What's he up to?"

"I don't know, but he ought to stop. It's made him cranky and flatulent."

"The girls are all on the TV tonight," Ryan said, still nursing a wound from earlier that night when Ryan's affections had been uncommonly piqued by a girl he had met at the bar at that night's concert. She was in her late twenties, tall, Mediterranean and sexy. This didn't make her much different from his usual fare, apart from her dark hair, but something about her intensity had made him respond to her in a way that had surprised Adam, who had never before seen Ryan's interest so possessed by a road girl.

Ryan had listened intently when she spoke and had looked earnestly into her eyes as they sat in the back of the van on the way to the hotel. He had been enchanted, as unbelievable as it had seemed to Adam.

Once at the hotel, however, her attitude, which had been only marginally interested in Ryan, became perturbed by the evening's lack of excitement.

"This is fucking stupid!" she had shouted. "You call yourselves rock stars? I've partied with rock stars before. This is fucking ridiculous. You all are pathetic."

She had collected her things, muttering, "I can't believe I came here with you. I should have known you all weren't shit when I saw you had a fucking van instead of a bus."

She had left the room and called for a taxi on her phone as she walked to the elevators. Ryan had watched her go, his pride wounded and his feelings hurt.

"I really liked her," he had said more to himself than to Adam, who witnessed the event. "Why couldn't I realize that she was going to be a total bitch?"

To medicate his insecurity, Ryan had taken to nursing a bottle of Southern Comfort and watching TV, hoping to forget his momentary indiscretion.

Adam collapsed into a chair and lit a cigarette.

"Non-smoking," Ryan said.

"What?"

"It's a non-smoking room," Ryan said, distracted by the TV listings.

Adam looked to the dresser where there was a coffee pot littered with stale cigarette butts floating in a pool of browning water.

Ryan continued scanning the pay-per-view porno selections. "Fist-Fuckers Incorporated," he said.

"What?"

Ryan sighed. "Just wishful thinking. Earlier I thought I saw 'Fellatio, Feces, and Ferrets.'"

Adam flicked his cigarette, sending ash flitting down upon the carpeting.

"Fuck me where I shit," Ryan said.

Struck with inspiration, Adam jumped to his feet and grabbed the whiskey from between Ryan's legs.

"Leprosy Lesbians Part Four. I guess some titles are tamer than others," Ryan continued.

Adam drew deeply from the whiskey and handed it back to Ryan. He then charged out of the room, imbued with renewed ambition to save the evening from an unacceptable lack of excitement.

"Super Sexy Slut Patrol," came Ryan's faint words as the door swung shut behind Adam.

The young man passed through the lobby, pleasantly adrift in thoughts of how fortuitous life could be, how rewarding and satisfying happiness was when one embraced life's opportunities.

It was summer. He was vacationing with his wife. They were newlyweds of nine months. She was asleep upstairs.

He couldn't explain to her why he had needed to leave on his present errand, why it had to be done at just this time, so late at night, when they had been pleasantly falling asleep in each other's arms. He had spared her the nature of his impulse because it would only have worried her. In truth, there was nothing to worry about. A man simply gets restless sometimes, he thought. A man needs to stretch his legs and feel himself somehow—and here is why he hadn't wanted to explain it to her and needlessly worry her with unwarranted doubts—free.

Sometimes the inside air can be oppressive, sometimes another's body heat suffocating.

There was no fissure in his love or his fidelity. Surely nothing could be farther from the truth. He simply had needed a moment to himself. This simple pleasure would only reaffirm his love for her, and after this brief soiree with the night, he would sleep better in her arms when he returned.

After some beseeching words she had relented, and he had left, crossing the threshold and striding complacently down the cool, air-conditioned hallway, a formidable resolve settling upon him.

In the lobby he nodded to the desk clerk, who did not return the gesture. The young man wasn't in the mood to be offended, and so he overlooked this minor breach of courtesy. Yet somewhere in the back of his mind, he noted a strange discomfort in the clerk's features that made him momentarily uneasy. However this too was soon supplanted by his overall good spirits.

He proceeded through the sliding glass doors that opened at his approach with a satisfying swoosh and left the moderated air for the humid summer air beyond.

His car was parked some distance away, around the corner from the main entrance of the hotel. As he walked farther from the entrance it became noticeably darker, and his eyes took some moments to adjust. The sky was overcast and moonless, and a few of the lights which lit the sprawling blacktop had gone out. The one closest to him interrupted the pleasant calm with a maddening electrical buzz as it flickered to life in brief staccato flashes before receding again to near darkness.

Alone as he was, his spirits became touched by a menacing possibility. He had the unshakable sensation that behind any of the silent cars there might be some nefarious congregation, some unseen crowd concealed behind the unsettling stillness.

He heard it first, a low murmur of voices carried along the wind from someplace ahead of him.

The voices were nearly inaudible, only occasionally distinct enough to allow him to isolate a few words here and there before they faded again into incoherence, resembling little more than the wind itself. He had just convinced himself that these voices were merely his imagination when he saw the dim light creeping from around the open door at the rear of a black trailer hitched behind a white van. He would have to pass this obstacle to reach his car—the rental—and though his good humor was not so easily dispelled, he was nonetheless aware of a diminishing sense of confidence as he approached.

"What's her name again?" one voice said.

"Faith," the other replied.

"That's ironic."

"Why?"

There was some grunting and shuffling.

"I just wasn't expecting that, is all. Now I feel kind of dirty for saying all that other stuff."

"*Now* you do. Be glad I didn't name her Helen Keller."

"Let's put her in one of the red shirts. I don't like those anyway. We shouldn't even sell them to the kids."

"But they do look good on the girls, don't they?" the other voice said. There was a small commotion and a muffled sound of chafing plastic that to the young man's ears resembled the timid belching of a saint. Then the same voice continued, "Goddamn, she's difficult. I just need to get this shirt on. She won't quit squirming."

"She's becoming one of us," the other voice said, his voice heavy. "Sad, really."

"Her innocence was about to expire," the other said. "She wouldn't have lasted much longer with hair and lips like that."

"And with those three or four accessible orifices."

The young man now stood in the darkness just beyond the light cast from the trailer's interior. His approach had made the black trailer appear like a black altar aglow with the light that framed it from the other side.

He heard only two voices, of that he was sure, but he was also certain of an unspoken third. A woman. Faith.

The small scuffle continued, and the one said, "No, dude. Lay her down on the boxes and pull it down over her—"

"I *am*. The shirt's caught on something."

The young man told himself that he would turn back, that he would avoid the possibility of a confrontation. Then he heard them continue, and he was seized with a mixture of fear and curiosity.

"Goddamn, Faith. Why do you have to be so difficult?"

There was another sound of rubbing plastic.

"This is ridiculous. I'm in the right if I give her a taste of the back of my hand, right?"

"A man's got to have authority. He cannot doubt his woman's fidelity."

He heard a sound of flesh contacting with some surface, followed by a laugh.

The young man coughed and plunged forward, rounding the opened door ahead of him. He saw one man, his complexion dark and tawny, facing the interior of the trailer as he stood on the pavement outside. Before him, lying upon a dark box, was a woman, her legs spread apart to either side of his waist, fluttering and kicking as the dark man towering over her struggled with something at her torso.

Watching this scene was another. This man, pale even in the evening's light, or perhaps because of it, stood inside the trailer. He leaned over the other two, one arm above his head as he grasped the top outer edge of the trailer to support himself as he inspected his companion's progress.

The young man's breath caught in his throat, and he slowed his pace again, his determination lost. The pale one noticed him and stopped speaking. He looked in the man's direction.

"I've almost got it," the dark one continued, unaware. "The fucking sleeve was caught." Then, noticing that his friend's attentions were elsewhere, he asked, "What is it?"

He turned to look behind him, swiveling his torso and bringing the woman at his waist into the light.

The young man's eyes met her dead, upturned stare, and a slight cry issued from his throat.

She was blonde, her eyes blue, her skin fair. He was embarrassed and ashamed as he observed her. He saw a red t-shirt rolled up upon her chest, resting just above the red painting of her nipples.

Then the dark-skinned one spoke to him.

"She's being converted tonight." He raised her outstretched torso to his chest, and there again came the awful sound of plastic rubbing against plastic. With his other hand he turned her head to face the young man. "She's becoming one of us."

"Once you've come this far, there's no turning back," the pale one said, smiling.

"Want to join us?" the dark one asked.

"She's only got three good orifices, though," the other said, his smile fading. "I'm disappointed, too."

"She's a good woman."

"She might have had an accident, though. You aren't prejudiced, are you?"

"She just wants to be loved."

"You'd be amazed how many more there are just like her."

"And you're out here tonight, too."

The young man's mouth moved once, saying nothing, and then he lifted his suddenly heavy feet to continue on his way. He stumbled, recovered his balance, and walked past them, saying only, "Here I come," and this almost incomprehensibly and to himself.

When he at last reached the rental car after what seemed like an endless trek across a vast black desert, he searched his pockets in a daze for the keys he was sure must be there. When he pulled his hand from one pocket he held only the pink scrunchie that his wife had asked him to hold earlier when they were out to dinner. He could have sworn, as he paused to consider this, that her hair had been up when he had left her, held in place by the same elastic fabric he now held in his hand.

His other pocket was empty.

Unable to enter the car, he returned the way he had come. He passed by the trailer where he had had his strange encounter only minutes before and saw that the doors were closed and locked, the darkness about it complete. The stillness appeared not to have been disturbed, and there was no trace of either the men or the woman.

When he returned to his room, his wife greeted him warmly, coming out of the bathroom in her nightgown and grabbing him about the shoulders from behind as he passed.

"Hi, sweetie! I missed you," she said, kissing him on the back of his neck.

Her hair was down.

The young man gave her no reply. She let go of his shoulders and watched him go to the bed where he sat down, never looking at her.

"Sweetie?" his wife said. "What's wrong?"

He didn't answer, but looked at her sternly, some discernible shade of gloom clouding his face.

Pounding.

"Open this door!"

More pounding.

"Open the pod-bay doors, Hal. Nobody puts baby in a corner! Soylent Green is people! Don't cut the blue wire! *Ste-laaa*!"

The door opened and Adam stood face to face with Joe for the second time in thirty minutes. Joe's face was the portrait of consternation, bespectacled, pale and weary.

"Hey, good, you're still awake," Adam said. "Is Tanner in there?"

"*No!*" came the retort from within.

Adam charged past Joe, shouldering him into the door, and dove onto Tanner's bed, discerning only a small lump curled beneath the sheets.

"You limp-wristed mamma's boy! You can start acting like a man! Eat the cake! I said eat the goddamned cake!" he shouted, pummeling his fists into Tanner's ribs.

Adam's humor was lost on Joe, whose patience was gone. He shouted at Adam from the doorway, "Adam, get the *fuck* out of here! We're trying to sleep!"

Adam stood up on the bed and kicked Tanner in the shins before leaping to the floor.

"Right! I'll get you for that!" Tanner shouted with less conviction than he'd intended.

"If you want a piece of me, I'll be across the hall, pussy," Adam said. "Just knock twice."

"Fuck you, asshole!"

Joe approached Adam and grabbed him by the shoulders.

"Get your stinking paws off me, you damned dirty ape!" Adam protested, struggling against Joe.

Joe pushed Adam out of the room and into the hall.

"You don't understand. I could've had class. I could've been a contender. I could've *been* somebody!"

Joe stood in the doorway watching Adam as he ranted through interruptions of his own laughter, hardly able to keep his balance in a hallway that seemed to sway with him.

"What we've got here is failure to communicate. We're as mad as hell, and we're not going to take this, *anymore!*" Adam shouted, raising his fist in solidarity with the vacant eighth floor hallway. "You gotta fight the good fight! Here is something you can't understand! I *am* big; it's the *pictures* that got small! Forget it, Jake. This is Chinatown—"

An open hand silenced Adam's next words, creasing his face with the force of Joe's consternated exhaustion.

Adam staggered backward, catching his breath. He groped the air for a moment and looked at his friend.

"Something wrong?" he asked.

Another slamming door was the only response.

"Sir! I de-*mand* satisfaction!"

"Let's get Faith into the pool," Stubhy said.

"Do you think the cold water will make her nipples erect?" Jason asked.

"Would that make up for her lack of skull fuckability?"

"It'd be a start."

"You know," Stubhy said as they hopped the small fence encircling the outdoor pool, "there aren't too many people who could find something to be unsatisfied about with a goddamned blow-up doll."

"It's a matter of standards," Jason said. "Mine just happen to be a little more refined."

Stubhy ignored this last insult and produced a small bottle of lighter fluid from his pocket. He tossed Faith onto a deckchair and walked over to a table where there was a small stack of plastic bowls. Picking them up, he asked, "You got the Polaroid?"

Jason produced a rather large and awkward-looking contraption. "Check."

"Can you get Faith?"

Jason cradled the camera in one hand and retrieved Faith from the chair with the other. "Swimming lessons, sweetie."

"This is more than a swimming lesson," Stubhy said, walking to where Jason stood near the edge of the pool.

He knelt and placed the bowls upside-down in the water so that they floated like miniature icebergs. He clustered them together, arranging a total of five. Next he took the lighter fluid and doused the undersides of the plastic bowls that now floated above the water's surface.

"Are you sure this is going to work?" Jason asked.

"No. Why? Do you doubt me?"

Jason bit his lip. He knew what Stubhy wanted to say, and he didn't want to extend an invitation to say it.

"You have the bottle rockets?"

"Of course," Jason said.

Jason lay down Faith so that she floated on the surface of the water. Holding her near the pool's edge with one hand, he placed five bottle rockets into her gaping mouth so that they each pointed in different directions, arranging them like a bouquet of flowers.

Before he could stop himself, Jason asked, "Are you sure the sparks won't burn through her skin?"

Almost before the words had left Jason's mouth, Stubhy answered, "Faith, Jason. You've got to have faith."

Jason rolled his eyes.

"Besides," Stubhy continued, "I told you, she's top of the line."

Jason withdrew his lighter. "When you're ready," he said.

"Place her between two of these," Stubhy said, and Jason moved Faith between two of the now flammable bowls. "First we light the bowls and push them away, then we light the bottle rockets."

Jason lit the exposed underside of the bowls before him, and to his surprise, they ignited, becoming two flaming islands on the water. He pushed these out toward the center of the pool as Stubhy did the same with his. By some miracle they fanned out before them, forming a convenient gap through which Faith could float.

Stubhy quickly lit the wicks of the bottle rockets in Faith's mouth and gently pushed her after the flaming beacons.

"Get the camera ready," Stubhy said. "No one's going to believe this."

The wicks began to hiss and spark, illuminating Faith's face in strange and erotic shadows, and Stubhy had a moment of doubt when he thought they'd overdone it, that Faith would never survive. But the wicks climbed higher, and Faith still floated, approaching the cleft in the flaming icebergs ahead of her.

"Hurry!" Stubhy shouted.

"I'm turning it on," Jason said.

"You're going to miss it!"

"Got it! It's ready!" Jason cried. He lifted the camera, turned it upon Faith, and took the first picture.

The scene he captured was eerily beautiful, the lights from the pool casting shadows against the fires on its surface. Faith floated calmly between them, a bouquet of sparkling wicks lighting her face in alternating shadows, the gentle hiss of the burning wicks intermingling with the gentle lapping of pool water against the edges.

Jason took another picture, and the first wick touched the gun powder. The former tranquility was now interrupted by a loud, terrible screeching as the rocket lifted from Faith's mouth and soared into the night, cutting a harsh streak of light through the pitch. Two others quickly followed, and the fourth and fifth ignited upon the heels of these.

Stubhy cackled like a hyena, and Jason, smiling and laughing with him, took another photograph.

After a few fleeting moments of excitement, the flaming bergs were quickly extinguished, the water overtaking their melted tops with a final culminating hiss. Four patches of steam rose about Faith, who floated in near darkness, lit only from below.

"Long, fast and hard," Ryan said as Adam stormed back into the room. "These are some weak titles, man. If they're going to do porno, they might as well do it right, you know? I feel like I'm looking at a listing for Cinemax."

Without any more provocation than Ryan's apparent indifference to the night's waning energy, Adam knocked the remote control out of his hand and yanked the TV cord out of the wall.

In retaliation Ryan retrieved the remote control from the floor and threw it across the room to where Adam was now tampering with the alarm clock radio. The remote flew past his head and impacted with the wall, splintering into plastic shrapnel that fell to the ground in a small hail of confetti.

Adam either didn't have time to notice or had arrived at such a state of inebriation that the near collision did not register.

Ryan raised his arms above his head in victory. "It's about time some shit started to break around here! I was beginning to think that this place was a bust."

The room suddenly became filled with a loud blast of Latin Samba music, and Adam slammed the clock radio back down onto the night stand.

Next Adam picked up the phone. Two rooms away, a phone rang.

"So what're we going to watch?" Adam asked as he waited.

"Don't know," Ryan said. "How about a Lifetime original movie? Maybe one of those chicks will take off their clothes."

Adam didn't have time to dignify this with a response as Joe picked up the other end.

"Yeah?" Joe said.

"Oh, are you guys still awake?" Adam said.

"Adam, what the fuck?"

"Only kidding. Listen, put Tanner on the phone. I want to apologize."

There was a shuffling on the other end and Adam could hear Joe tell Tanner to take the phone. He heard some shouting and then Tanner's voice in the earpiece.

"Yeah?" Tanner said.

"What the fuck is this? I don't want to talk to you," Adam said.

"*What?*"

"I told Joe to tell you to go fuck yourself. Stop wasting my time, I'm trying to sleep."

"*You're* trying to—"

"If you were any kind of a man you'd come over here and fight me instead of lying in bed fondling your testicles. Ryan thinks you're a pussy, and he's got five dollars on me. Refusing to fight is as good as a forfeit, so—"

"Fuck *you!*" Tanner shouted. "I'm trying to *sleep!*"

"That's right, Tanner," Ryan called from the bed. "I just upped it to *ten!*"

"Ryan just heard you," Adam continued, "and he's disappointed. Stubhy's here and he thinks you sound like—how did you say it?" Adam paused as though listening to someone near him. "Right, a 'pussy ass little bitch,' is how he puts it. We're across the hall if you need us and—"

There was a clicking as the line went dead. Adam reached across to the nightstand and turned off the radio, motioning for Ryan to be quiet. They listened closely and heard a door slam nearby followed by loud pounding upon another nearby door.

A moment later there were muffled shouts and hostile obscenities from the hallway. This continued for some time more before another loud slamming of a door punctuated the man's final words.

In the silence that followed, Adam heard padded footsteps upon the carpeting in the hallway. They approached and stopped, ostensibly listening for some indication of life within, then proceeded farther off. A few seconds later they came back, and soon he heard the soft shutting of a door nearby.

Adam smiled and replaced the phone upon the night stand.

"What was that about?" Ryan asked.

"Satisfaction," Adam said, turning the radio on again.

"So it had nothing to do with your women the next morning, then," Ryan said.

Adam looked at Ryan. "How long have you been waiting to say that, Ryan? Why don't you go find yourself another fat chick? They're not exactly at a premium here in Louisiana."

"That was only once and that was because it was Wisconsin," Ryan said. "You don't have too many options in that state, you know."

"Yeah, but they don't all have buckteeth and skin-tags."

"If only ... See, this is why people accuse you of being an asshole. All women are beautiful."

Adam looked to the bottle in Ryan's lap. "So is that the Southern Comfort philosophy of sexual indiscrimination?"

"I never took you for the jealous type," Ryan said, picking up a shoe and taking aim at the power button on the TV.

Standing to retrieve his cigarettes from the chair in the corner, Adam struck his hip on the desk to his left.

"God*damnit*!"

"Damn, Teenwolf!" Ryan said, a mouthful of whiskey exploding from his mouth. "That's karma! Score one for the fat girls! You're an asshole!"

Nursing his hip, Adam was struck with another idea.

"We got any more beer?" he asked.

"Fuck yeah, we got more beer," Ryan said, launching his shoe at the television where it connected squarely with the power button.

"I'm turning this place into a bar."

Ryan reclined against the bed's headboard and picked up the telephone as Adam, possessed with inspiration, began dragging the desk across the carpeting and out of the door.

Following the aberration of flaming bowls and bottle rockets that came from the area of the outdoor pool, Stubhy, Jason and Faith found the front desk unattended. They had left the pool unhurried but aware that their welcome had expired, and as they rounded the west corner of the hotel, the desk attendant, accompanied by the assistant manager who had been dozing behind his desk when the sounds had erupted, emerged through the south doors that led directly into the pool area.

Stubhy lit a cigarette as he passed the unattended front desk, and using a piece of scotch tape from the dispenser on the counter, he taped the smoking cigarette to the inside of Faith's mouth. He then placed Faith behind the counter so that she stood before the computer terminal, facing the entrance, a small bouquet of plastic flowers to her right.

Jason took two more pictures and laid one of the Polaroids on the counter.

When the phone started ringing, they lifted Faith back over the counter and proceeded toward the elevators.

Tanner had been calling the front desk for several minutes, and when he didn't receive an answer after several tries, he became only more determined to receive a response. At last, a hurried voice answered.

"Yes? Hello? Front desk."

"Yes," Tanner began, speaking in the most professional voice he could manage. "I'm afraid there's a gentleman in the room across from ours, room 831, who has taken all of the furniture out of his room and stacked it up in front of our doorway."

"I beg your pardon?"

"Quite a lot of it, too—desks, end-tables, chairs. I think I saw a coffee-maker underneath the ironing board."

Tanner heard some murmuring as the person on the other end spoke to someone near him.

"Hello?"

Returning to the phone, the person said, "Yes. I'm sorry sir. You were saying?"

"Room 831, yes. He stacked his furniture outside of our door. I think he'd intended to barricade us inside of our room, you know, but the doors open inward, not outward, and so it kind of defeats the purpose. I don't mean to complain, really, but it's just a little inconvenient. I think that if there were a fire it might be dangerous."

In front of room 830, two doors down the hall from Adam and Ryan, there stood a strange postmodern assemblage of desks, chairs, end-tables, garbage cans, lamps and one upturned solid oak dresser, the preternatural nature of this last artifact bearing the mystery of an Easter Island giant head, prompting one to question how one man might have managed to move it there and then lift in onto its side, and for what macabre purpose?

This was a question that would plague future observers in the hours to come.

"You say that all of this furniture is stacked in front of your door?"

"Yes."

Incredulous, the desk clerk said, "Alright, sir, we'll look into this. I'm sorry for the inconvenience."

Tanner replaced the receiver, and in the dark his hazy mind saw retribution. Tanner didn't think that there would be any need for police, but Tanner also thought that professional wrestling was a legitimate sport.

Jason pressed the button for floor number nine, and while Stubhy readjusted Faith's t-shirt, her cigarette now clenched firmly between his teeth, Faith's hand fondled the keypad. As he adjusted the collar so that the Lucky Boys Confusion slogan was centered across her chest, he exerted enough pressure on her arm so that Faith's hand depressed the button for floor number eight.

When the bell announced their arrival they stepped from the elevator without noticing the error.

"What now?" Jason asked. "I say we hang her from the ceiling near the elevators, as a warning to other dissidents."

"Dissidents?"

"Better yet, let's impale her on a stake. She's already made for it anyway."

Stubhy ignored Jason as he turned into the hallway, the elevator doors closing behind them.

Jason was about to say something more when they both stopped, their eyes falling upon the strange construction halfway down the hall.

"What the fuck is that?" Stubhy asked.

Jason didn't have any guesses, and so they approached the bizarre assemblage in silence. When they stood before it, they remarked upon it in low, muted voices like two visitors to a museum of modern art.

"It's sort of cool," Jason said.

"I wonder what it means," Stubhy said.

They stood for a moment in silence, and then Stubhy said, "I think it's a comment on modernity. It's just an assorted pile of shit that doesn't mean anything."

"Okay."

"But it does mean something, because someone put it here."

"I guess."

"They want to show that when art tries to deny an author, it becomes an object. But you can't look at this and not think that someone put it here on purpose," Stubhy said. "So its meaninglessness is a comment on its meaning."

"The author doesn't matter," Jason said. "It has no life without us."

"If the author doesn't matter and it wouldn't have meaning without us, then it's only an object and not art."

"It's meaning isn't fixed. It's up to us," Jason said. "We give it meaning, and it can mean a variety of things."

"That's bullshit. If that were true, you wouldn't need an author. There wouldn't be a variety of meanings, but rather no meanings at all. Objects in nature don't mean anything until they become symbols endowed with agency. The only meanings that aren't fixed are misinterpretations."

"Well," Jason said, considering. "Maybe you're right. If there's a meaning, I think the author meant for us to burn it."

Stubhy considered this. "You're right."

"Do we have any more lighter fluid?"

"I think we're out."

Jason's countenance fell.

Stubhy stepped forward and placed Faith upon the haphazard assemblage, contorting the limbs and maneuvering the damp shirt so that the LBC logo could easily be read. When he had finished, he stepped back, and he and Jason observed the work. There was a discernable look of pride in Stubhy's eyes.

"How did you manage to hold her legs in place like that?" Jason asked.

"First I placed her waist so that it would be at eye level. It's important to capture a viewer's interest early. Then I spread her legs apart and weaved them through the legs of that upturned chair, there," he said, pointing, "and that lamp over there."

After spreading her legs apart at forty-five degree angles from her waist, Stubhy had then positioned Faith's left arm so that it seemed to rest just above her most feminine orifice, pointing, perhaps playfully, perhaps petulantly, perhaps invitingly. Her other arm was splayed out to her side and her head was angled backward so that she looked toward the ceiling, her face the same constant expression of permanent ecstasy.

"She looks like another satisfied LBC fan," Stubhy said, clearly proud.

"She looks like she's on an altar waiting to be sacrificed."

"We'll leave her here. She's better than a bumper sticker or a billboard. She's a poster child."

"Woman," Jason said. "A poster *woman*. I don't think you should call her a child."

"Right. She's more like a post-menopausal white-trash speed freak mother of six."

Jason nodded. "You've got to love our fans."

Jason raised the camera and took a final picture for posterity, leaving Faith for those who would discover her later.

"Ain't—No—Holla—Back—Girl," Adam said as he wrote the words.

"Yeah," Ryan said into the phone. "Now Adam's writing obscenities in shaving cream on the wall."

"This way, nobody has to ask," Adam said, stepping back and regarding his work. "They'll know."

"He looks like a teenage tagger," Ryan said.

Adam stepped forward again, shaking the canister, and began crafting a smiley-face that would ultimately prove too big for his rapidly diminishing supply of shaving cream. While making the mouth, arguably the most integral part of the smiley-face trademark, his reservoir went dry. Frustrated, Adam flung the empty Gillette canister across the room where it nearly collided with a wall-mounted lamp that hung near Ryan's head. With all of the furniture except for the bed now removed from their room, the lights cast a morbid shadow upon the wall, illuminating two misplaced and uneven eyes and one poorly sculpted hair-lip mouth receding into crooked nothingness.

"Now for a little-known fact," Adam said, searching his pockets. "Shaving cream is flammable."

"You really shouldn't have called the front desk, Tanner," Joe said into the darkness, half asleep.

"Yes, I should have!" Tanner protested. "Adam needs to be taught a lesson. He can't just barge in here and expect everyone to cater to his will!"

"But you told them that it was the guy across the hall. He had every right to yell at you. Why the fuck were you pounding on his door at this hour?"

"I thought it was Adam's room. And anyway, the guy threatened to cut off my dick and shove it down my throat!"

"That's probably not the first time someone's said that to you."

"But this guy doesn't even *know* me. When they figure out it wasn't the guy across the hall they'll go next door or something anyway. They'll figure it out."

"I still think it was a bad idea."

"What's the worst they're going to do? They'll make him put it all back," Tanner said. "So what?"

Joe was uneasy at this, but his want of sleep prevailed.

"Yeah, but we don't know what else they might have done."

Joe drifted back into sleep, and Tanner retreated into the security of his conviction.

The young man couldn't sleep. He started from another fitful sleep in another agitated spasm, ejaculating a stifled cry.

An arm lay across him. He looked down at his wife and listened to her breathing. It was slow, rhythmic, tranquil and content. Inside his own chest his heart raced and fluttered, trying to escape, trying to fly the torments of his thoughts.

And it had been only nine months. He should still be enamored with every quiet moment of peaceful belonging.

He slipped out of bed, careful not to disturb his wife's sleep, delicately replacing her arm upon a pillow. In the bathroom, without turning on the light, he splashed his face with cold water, avoiding his shadowy reflection in the mirror.

He needed to go out, to get free of the room.

He found his shoes and carefully unlocked the door, opening it only as far as was necessary to allow him to pass around it, keeping the hallway lights from potentially disturbing his wife.

After easing the door shut with only the slightest clicking of the latch, he listened for any sound of life or movement from behind it, his ear pressed against the cold metal surface. When no sound came, he breathed deep and exhaled a soft sigh, feeling a slight weight lift from him.

She remained secure and in the dark.

Not wishing to return outdoors, he walked down the hallway toward the stairs. He would get his relief from walking the secure hallways of the hotel until he felt himself better suited to return to sleep, and to his wife.

Adam lay on his back in the middle of a floor now cleared of unnecessary debris and obstacles.

His arms lay outstretched to his sides, his legs spread apart in the posture of some miscreant angel trying to leave his impression in a snowless pasture. He held a burning cigarette in one hand and a fresh bottle of beer in the other. He relished the satisfaction of a Herculean labor accomplished, a recalcitrant opponent vanquished. This, he thought, would teach Tanner and

Joe. In his mind, this was ample retribution for his earlier mistreatment.

"I think it'd be cool to have a stalker," Ryan said. He had finished his bottle of Southern Comfort and was now well into the beers he shared with Adam. "It'd be flattering, you know?"

"Some of these groupies already fill that bill," Adam said.

"But I mean the real thing. These crazy groupie chicks are like the little leagues. A genuine stalker—that's how you know you've arrived. I'm talking about a chick with a knife."

Adam grimaced. "What the hell is *wrong* with you?"

"What's wrong with me?" Ryan retorted. "*You* just took all the furniture out of our room and stacked it in front of Tanner and Joe's room, you fucking lunatic."

Adam smiled. "Yeah. I totally did, didn't I?"

Salsa music poured into the silences between them. The toes of Adam's right foot tapped visibly beneath the thin canvas of his sneaker.

Ryan reached for another beer and picked up the phone as Adam lit another cigarette.

"Time to call Tanner again. What's their room number?" Ryan asked, punching three numbers into the pad at the same time that Adam's hand discovered a package of Ryan's bottle rockets lying just underneath a corner of the bed.

Ryan cradled the phone on his shoulder while the other end rang.

Adam held a rocket in one hand and lit the wick, grinning at the satisfying crackle as the fire began its ascent.

Ryan heard a groggy, gravely voice answer.

"Joe?" Ryan said, surprised. "For fuck's sake, you sound like a goddamned mariner."

The wick caught the fuse and there was a loud screaming hiss as the rocket slipped from Adam's hand, flying to the ceiling where it bounced and then turned toward Ryan just as there erupted a loud and thunderous roar from the other end of the receiver. Ryan shouted and covered his eyes with his forearm as the rocket whizzed past his head, scurried along the wall toward the window and finally exploded.

The raging tirade from the other end of the line ended abruptly with a sharp clicking, and Ryan looked bewildered for a moment. "I guess I had the wrong room," he said.

He looked at the phone pad again and began punching in a stream of numbers. Several minutes later, in the midst of his conversation with the person on the other end, he said, "Adam, do you want to say hello to Saarang from Swizzle Tree?"

"Fuck yeah, I do!"

Ryan, a meditating Buddha connected long-distance to the Midwest, held the telephone cord several inches from its base and swung the receiver above his head like Roy Rogers wielding a lasso, a sinister smile on his face. This terrific gyroscope whizzed several times above his head before making its first contact with the wall lamp beside the bed, smashing the light into a cascade of broken glass.

Unaware that he had disconnected the telephone from the wall at some point in the process, Ryan pulled the receiver back up to his ear and asked, "Holy shit, could you hear that? Hello? Hello?" When he was met with silence, he said to Adam, "Dude, they hung up. You better call them back."

"I don't *do* that!" Adam exclaimed from the floor, pointing to the message written in shaving cream on the wall. "I thought I'd made that clear."

Ryan paused. "Oh. Is that what that shit means?"

Adam shifted uncomfortably. "I don't know. I think so."

Ryan disregarded the issue and commenced swinging the phone again with slow, deliberate oscillations. Increasing his speed and taking aim, he drew his arm quickly behind him and the plastic missile followed, connecting squarely into the metal, glass and drywall of a second lamp.

Ryan brought the telephone back up to his ear, but the line was still dead.

There was one remaining light in the room. It was mounted on the wall near Adam, who still lay in the space once occupied by the dresser. Now confident of his skill, Ryan took careful aim, and Adam's chest and legs soon felt a small rain of broken glass.

Darkness descended upon the room, and Adam, cackling below, choked on a mouthful of beer.

"Dude, it's too dark in here now," Adam said after clearing his throat.

"Fuck it. It's time to go to sleep anyway."

"But it's too early," Adam said, struggling against the phlegm collecting at the back of his throat.

An alcohol stupor overcame him, and he drifted into unconsciousness.

The young man had walked several floors. He felt more relaxed, the calm meditation and repetition of pacing each floor having the effect of mollifying the itinerant spirits within him.

He walked each floor from one end to the other, tracing the U-shaped floor plan, and entered the stairwells at either end to descend from one floor to the next. He had made his way through five such cycles when he stepped out of the stairwell and onto the eighth floor.

As he approached the first corner at the end of the hall, a strange fear gripped his chest. Rounding the corner, he abruptly stopped.

Before him, some fifteen feet away, stood the strange construction outside of room 830. Along with one floor lamp, a desk and a table lamp, there was a television, a mirror, a pastel painting of a summer cottage and, impressively, a large oak dresser standing on its side. There were other small accoutrements peppered among these, but what captured his immediate attention and held him frozen in place was the specter of Faith perched like a fallen angel atop some demoniac Christmas tree.

He stared, paralyzed, and all of his former misfortunes prevailed upon him. He felt the cold embrace of despair, suddenly aware that he had been away from his wife for far too long that night, aware that he had left her alone and vulnerable and susceptible to her own dissolute impulses. The phantasm before him, haunting him throughout this terrible night which should have been spent so happily in his wife's arms, had become a menacing curse of doubts and accusations.

He turned to retrace his path back the way he'd come.

As the door to the stairwell into which he'd retreated closed behind him, the loud and sonorous clicking of the latch echoing in the hollow stillness, a bell sounded and a light illuminated above the elevator doors on the eighth floor.

The young man ascended the several flights of stairs to his own floor, and the exertion did his mind some good. His wife didn't move when he returned and took his place beside her in their bed, but her silence seemed artificial, her body, as he brushed against it, too rigid.

He stared up into the bleak darkness of the room before falling into a tormented sleep, dreaming dreams of gloom.

Pounding.

Adam sat up and heard a gentle waterfall of broken glass spill from his chest.

More pounding.

Darkness surrounded him, and somewhere nearby Latin music struggled through a single speaker interspersed with abrasive, crackling static.

"Please open the door, sir," a voice called from outside. "We have the police with us."

Adam's mind struggled to comprehend as he flipped open his cell phone and called Lucky Boys Confusion's manager. He had come to join them on the road for a few shows, and he had been asleep one floor above for several hours.

A weak and tired voice answered.

"Jeff?" Adam said.

"Yeah?"

"It's Adam."

"What is it? It's like, four in the morning."

"I think the police are outside of my hotel room."

"Yeah?" There was a pause. "Why are they there?"

In Adam's mind he heard the faint echo of a past conversation. Jeff, their newfound manager, had discussed the music industry and his experience with it during one of their first conversations several months back. These were the words that now played in Adam's mind.

"The one thing I can't stand," Jeff had said, "is when bands get fucked up and trash their hotel rooms. That really pisses me off. Everyone wants to be *The Who*, you know what I mean? It's just such a cliché."

If Adam remembered nothing else of that early conversation, he remembered this. At the time, Adam had offered his sincere accord.

But that was before Teenwolf, before the road and before a slap in the face.

"Adam?"

"Yeah?"

"Why are they there?" Jeff asked again.

Temporizing, Adam said, slowly, "I don't know."

He trailed off, struggling to recall the events of the past few hours. His mind raced at a snail's pace through sleep and beer, reaching for answers. Remembering the broken glass in his lap, he made a hazy epiphany. It was a horrible realization that dawned upon him with the furtive impact of an archaic leviathan slipping to the surface of a Scottish Loch.

The police, he thought, were probably going to consider this hotel room trashed.

"Adam?" the phone said again.

"It's probably nothing. I wouldn't worry about it, just go back to sleep. Sorry to wake you."

"Let me know how it turns out," Jeff said, hanging up.

The police knocked again, louder.

"Hey, Ryan," Adam said.

Ryan was half-awake, still groggy and searching his own recollection for answers.

"Yeah?"

"We got anymore beer?"

"Fuck yeah, we've got more—"

The door opened, spilling harsh light into the dark room. A moment later a flashlight beam shot into various corners of the room, first witness to the horrors within.

Adam sat upon the floor in a field of glass shards that glistened in the light that passed over them. Ryan, his head cloudy and his eyes tired, sat up in bed, patiently awaiting this new spate of misfortune.

"Turn on a light," a voice said.

"There aren't any," another responded.

"Shit. I'll get a light bulb."

"Gentlemen?"

"Yes?" Adam said, trying to sound indignant. "Is there a problem?"

The flashlight toured the room and returned to Adam.

"Where is all of the furniture for your room?"

"I'd like to know the very same thing," he said. "It was like this when we got here. This is a goddamned outrage and I should like to speak with management immediately."

The flashlight drifted slowly to the wall to Adam's left, its spotlight tracing Adam's message scrawled in shaving cream.

"Why don't you do me a favor and just stay where you are until we can get some proper light in here."

"Suit yourself," he said. "It's about time we received some proper attention around here."

Adam sat on the edge of the bed, his hands cuffed behind his back, the entire room lit by a single, shadeless hundred-watt bulb. Ryan was outside in the hallway fielding an interrogation for his apparent participation in Adam's madness.

When asked why he had moved all of their furniture out of the room and attempted to barricade the sleeping patrons of 830 inside of their room, Adam had replied, "Because they're crazy. They have rabies and countless STD's. I was trying to protect the other guests. They had designs on the virgins on the fifth floor. You ought to be *thanking* me."

When asked about the inflatable sex toy perched atop the furniture, Adam had been legitimately perplexed and tried to recall if he had placed it there. In the end he considered that it must have been Ryan's and that he had placed it there sometime after he had fallen asleep.

Now Adam was alone, and handcuffed.

The voices outside discussed punishments as they dismantled Adam's sculpture, replacing the furniture to its proper, upright position. He heard a voice say, "Jesus, he even grabbed the coffee-maker and the iron."

Adam lifted himself off of the bed and swung his hands underneath his thighs. He then rolled back upon the bed, lifted his legs into the air and swung his arms around them before pitching forward again so that his hands were now in his lap in front of him. With his hands now more accessible, he reached into his pocket and retrieved his cigarettes. He withdrew a Parliament with an unencumbered ease, his fingers working against the metal restraints of the handcuffs with the agility of a magician manipulating a deck of cards, and placed the cigarette in his mouth before realizing that, like earlier, he had no lighter. In retrospect, he considered it fortunate that he hadn't been able to find a lighter when he had wanted to set the wall on fire, but now he only wanted to light his cigarette.

Adam scanned the room and saw, upon the floor near the remains of a broken lamp, his Ray-Ban sunglasses. He rolled off the bed and retrieved them, placing them on his face, and from this kneeling position a flash of green caught his eye. There, beneath an edge of the bedspread, Adam discovered his misplaced lighter.

"There you are, you sonofabitch," he said, crawling over to retrieve it.

He sat back down on the edge of the bed and lit his cigarette. This done, he awkwardly tossed the lighter back across the room.

When the officer came back into the room, he stopped. He looked at Adam, observing his disheveled black hair, black t-shirt and black denim jeans. He took another moment to ponder the dark aviator sunglasses and the cigarette now smoldering between his lips.

The two men looked at each other for a moment, the one divining the creature before him, the other giving him silence and space to do so. Then, helping to ease the tension, Adam grunted an apologetic "oh," and in one swift acrobatic maneuver he replaced his hands behind his back, nodding understanding to the officer when he'd finished, the cigarette still clenched securely between his teeth.

A touch of amusement creased the officer's face, and he stepped aside to readmit the hotel assistant manager into the room.

"Why is there a chair in the stairwell on the fifth-floor landing?" he asked. There was no amusement in his voice.

"I couldn't *feng shui* it with the others," Adam said through clenched teeth. "It was too awkward and unbalanced. You ought to have some proper chairs in this place, you know? I thought this was a high-class dig."

Hostile and defensive, the man said, "Well, it didn't break, otherwise you'd be paying for that, too. I'd say the chairs here are just fine."

Adam shrugged, exhaling smoke, his eyes comfortably veiled. "If that's your standard."

"And why is he smoking?" the man asked, looking at the officer. "This is a non-smoking room!"

The officer, visibly tired, intervened. "Okay, we're going to take you two outside to the squad car while we go over some paperwork." Looking to the two suitcases which supplied the only relative furniture in the room apart from the bed, he asked, "Are these all of your things?"

The officer handed them to the assistant manager to carry downstairs.

Adam and Ryan sat in the back of a squad car.

When they had been inside talking with the police, Ryan had appeared contrite and apologetic, if not to the hotel then to himself for having allowed their havoc to escalate unchecked. But in the Louisiana squad car, out from under the gaze of scrutinizing parties, he turned to Adam with a grin.

"Dude, they're *pissed*."

"I don't know. But the cop doesn't really seem to care," Adam said.

"I don't mean him. I mean the hotel people."

"What do you think they're going to do?"

Ryan looked into the lobby where the officer discussed matters with the assistant manager. "I don't know. When you think about it, we didn't really destroy much. Just some light bulbs and maybe a lamp."

"We have a way of making it look worse than it really is."

"But where did you get that doll?" Ryan asked. "I didn't even see you with it."

Adam turned to him. "*Me*? I thought that was *you*."

Ryan shook his head. "No. But she was wearing an LBC shirt. Isn't that weird?"

"Maybe it was Joe's, then."

When the officer and the manager had reached some sort of agreement, the officer exited the lobby and approached the car. Opening the door to let them out, he said, "Okay, boys. Seems you've gotten lucky this time. They're not going to press charges. They're going to settle for evicting you and holding you accountable for damages. Just try not to step on their toes too much while we finish this up or they might change their minds."

"No dice," Adam said.

"Nope," Ryan said. "We demand a full apology and a free night's stay."

"The Presidential Suite."

"With free wet bar privileges."

"And who was that cute Mexican maid we saw earlier?"

"We want her number."

They looked at the officer for his reaction. The officer smiled and shook his head.

"That's just what I mean," he said. "Don't make my life any more difficult."

"Don't worry," Ryan said. "You can trust us."

"We're your friends."

Adam sat beside Ryan in the manager's office, and the officer sat across from them. Assistant manager Alan, according to his nametag, was visibly incensed as he sat behind his desk, scribbling information on triplicate forms.

The officer smiled at Adam and Ryan, and a playful light came into his eyes.

"You boys need to find a more constructive use of your time," he said, leaning back.

Alan's eyes left his papers for a moment to look suspiciously at the officer.

"We know," Ryan said. "Things just kind of got out of hand."

"Well, 'getting out of hand,' as you call it, shouldn't entail extensive property damage," Alan said. "And perhaps you'd like to explain these, too?" he said, pushing two Polaroids of Faith across the desk toward them.

Adam picked them up, and after overcoming his initial surprise, he began to laugh. He passed the first, showing Faith's baptism, to Ryan, who also began to laugh. The second picture showed her behind the front desk, and even the officer had to chuckle at their reactions.

"I have no idea," Adam said. "I swear I don't know where she came from."

"She looks like a Cincinnati girl to me," Ryan said.

"I think that's being a little generous," Adam said. "She looks like she might have all of her teeth."

"Well, someone was disturbing our other guests with that doll," Alan said, irritated by their flippant attitude. "Could be considered trespassing, even."

"Trespassing?" Adam said.

"Who? The doll?" Ryan said.

"Did she do any damage?" Adam asked. "I mean, other than … What did she do again?"

Alan glared at them and looked at the officer to see if he would support him. Fuming, he returned to his paperwork.

"It all seems like pretty innocent stuff to me," Ryan said.

"Well, whoever it was, was in the pool area after-hours. It's trespassing," Alan said without looking up.

"Apart from dusting her for fingerprints or semen, I don't know what to tell you," Adam said. "I honestly don't know where the doll came from."

Adam hoped that, to save them some headache, a connection would not be made between the doll's t-shirt and their band. Then, as if reading his mind, the officer spoke up again.

"You boys look like you're a part of some rock and roll group," he said.

"Lucky Boys Confusion," Ryan said, smiling knowingly at Alan's downturned head.

The officer chuckled. "You all are big?"

"We play the House of Blues tomorrow."

"No fooling?" the officer said, genuinely impressed.

"You listen to much rock n' roll?" Ryan asked.

"I'm not sure you boys would know much of the stuff that I was into in my day. I was always partial to the Rolling Stones, though."

"Of course," Ryan said. "They're amazing."

"You can't beat Satisfaction." Adam said.

"Or Paint it Black," Ryan added. "You listen to much Dylan?"

"Oh, sure!" the officer said, proud. "That's where The Rolling Stones got their name from, you know."

Ryan smiled and nodded, considering it not worth correcting this common error. "That's right. I always lump Dylan and Cash together, you know. Just that classic sort of rockin' feel. Even if they sometimes call them 'folk' and 'country,' it's all rock n' roll to me," Ryan said, beating a rhythm on his thighs and tapping his foot.

"Now Johnny Cash is in another league altogether," the officer said rapturously. "That man was—no, *is* a legend. The man in black. You know, Folsom Prison Blues is one of my all-time favorite songs."

"When we were in Memphis we visited the old Sun Studios," Ryan said. "I remember thinking, 'this is where Johnny Cash and Jerry Lee Lewis and Elvis fucking Presley recorded! This is fucking awesome!'"

"I've been there myself!" the officer exclaimed. "A long time ago. Probably before you were even born. And I saw Johnny Cash over in Mississippi, back in his heyday. No kidding. That was a few years back too, of course, when I was something of a little hellion myself. But I reckon I'll remember every detail of that night until the day I die, no matter how senile I get!" He leaned back in his chair again, laughing softly, lost to a memory that was all his own.

Alan's pen ran out of ink, and with a force intended to be more emphatic than he could muster, he threw the pen into the wastebasket beside his desk.

"But I have to admit that today I'm more of a blues man, myself," the officer continued.

"Well, you can't get away from the blues influence on rock n' roll, anyway," Ryan said. "It's the old rhythm and blues, foot-stompin' guitar and drums. Hell, Robert Johnson is one of the first rock n' rollers in my book."

The officer marveled at the reference. "Robert Johnson could play guitar like nobody's business," he said in a reverential tone. "If he sold his soul to the Devil for it, it was worth it. The devil dog howl, you know."

"Elvis just managed to capture the old bluesman grooves and add one hell of a stage presence," Adam said.

"Now Elvis *was* a legend. But he never sustained the dignity of a Johnny Cash," the officer said.

"Dying on the shitter with a belly full of pills sort of decimates your icon image, I guess," Ryan said.

"That and marrying a girl before she's old enough to drive a car," Adam added.

"He and Jerry Lee Lewis, I guess. But Jerry's girl was his cousin," the officer said.

"Kissing cousins," Ryan said. He turned to Adam, "You've got some cute cousins, don't you? Maybe you could—"

"How do you spell your last name again?" Alan said to Adam, interrupting.

"So you all are playing the House of Blues in New Orleans, eh?" the officer said, ignoring Alan. "It's a good place?"

"Awesome," Adam said. "One of our favorite venues in the country."

"Second only to the Metro in Chicago," Ryan added.

"You know," Adam said, "if you wanted, we could put you on the guest list tomorrow night."

The man's eyes noticeably widened. "No fooling! You'd do that?"

"Absolutely, man."

"You'd have a great time," Ryan said. "You might even like us."

"Well, hot damn! I haven't been to a rock n' roll show in years! You think my wife could come, too?"

Adam guffawed. "Of course. We'll put you on the guest list plus one. We'll get you backstage access and everything."

"Really?" he asked, incredulous.

"It's no problem. Just give us your name and we'll set you up."

The officer eagerly withdrew his wallet and produced a black card with a gold police star emblazoned in the center. The name on the card, written in gold, read 'Connor McCool.'

"The name's Irish," he said, noticing Adam's incredulous pause as he read it.

Alan, feeling ignored, pushed a set of documents across his desk.

"They'll need to sign here," he said, pointing to specific portions of the page with a fresh Bic pen. "And initial here, sign here and here and then ..."

Alan fumbled with more papers. His blue shirt was unbuttoned at the top, and he appeared constricted by cuffs that he continually pushed up his arm, fighting the binding that restricted his movements. He was young, perhaps only ten years older than Adam and Ryan, and he seemed to have taken their actions as a personal affront.

"Because you know, you'll have to pay fifty dollars in extra clean-up fees, two-hundred dollars in damages and sign this acceptance of culpability," Alan continued.

"I've never been backstage at a rock concert before," Officer McCool said to no one in particular.

"And of course, you'll have to leave the premises when we're through. And you won't be welcomed back," Alan said.

"My wife is going to get a kick out of this," Officer McCool added.

"Excuse me," Alan said to the officer. "Could you make sure that they provide accurate identification and credit card numbers to complete these documents? They need to understand that this is unacceptable behavior and extremely disruptive to—"

"Backstage," McCool said to himself.

"I'll need a credit card number for damages and—"

"I'm going to feel like a young boy all over again," he said. "Young and free, just like old times."

Throwing the Game

In June of 2000, Lucky Boys Confusion signed to Elektra records.

Since their days as a high school band playing VFW's and church basements, label representatives had been calling with smarmy vigor, dripping with promises and toting briefcases of fame. At the time the band had comported itself not unlike an adolescent female virgin, receiving suitors with considerable scrutiny and crossing their legs until assured that their choice would prove "the one."

The day they signed with Elektra was the moment that all bands, from their origins in friends' garages and parents' living rooms, dreamed about. This was their step to stardom, magazine covers and MTV. They were never naïve enough to think that this might all be accomplished with a single signature, but they understood that their determination and drive was an added asset and could not be criticized for the hope that shone in their eyes.

Jason, Joe, Adam, Ryan, Stubhy 1997

Adam and Stubhy started writing songs in May of 1997, and in June they recruited Ryan, the drummer from Stubhy's former band Farmboy. It had been a custom for Adam and me to attend a Farmboy show every week after discovering them the previous fall, and when we heard news that the band had broken up, Adam had proposed a collaboration between Stubhy and his own former band mate and guitarist, Joe Sell.

Joe, who Adam contends can solo over any piece of music, had been playing with Adam throughout high school in their own band, Spinning Jenny. The timing of Spinning Jenny and Farmboy's dissolution provided a unique opportunity to combine those elements from both bands—two groups of musicians who differed in as many styles and influences as they shared. After Stubhy recruited Jason to play bass, they had added the final, crucial element to complete their table of five strong legs. Jason's capability with the bass guitar, a skill often overlooked in rock bands that satisfy themselves on their bass player's ability to play roots and thirds, is arguably the component that gives many of Lucky Boys Confusion's songs that funk feel and the motion of a body-swaying, hip-swinging groove.

In September of 1997, Lucky Boys Confusion released their first four song EP containing the songs 40/80, Back Then, What Gets Me High and Dumb Pop Song. One night while driving from a party, Ryan mistakenly left seven or eight copies of this tape in the backseat of my car. Whether this was Ryan's particular brand of guerilla marketing or a legitimate drunken mistake, the tapes that shifted around the backseat of my car slowly disappeared into the hands of random curious passengers, and some undoubtedly became fans and supporters of the band thereafter. This was all part of the game of word-of-mouth promotion in the pre internet social networking age, and with it Lucky Boys Confusion began to garner a considerable fanbase in and around the suburban Chicagoland area. It was a big event when they played their first show in Madison, Wisconsin, a short time later because it was the first time that we would see the name Lucky Boys Confusion on a marquee and the first time that we would spend the night in a hotel, on the road, as part of the Lucky Boys Confusion party train.

Ryan. Drinking.

In October of 1998 they released their first LP, *Growing Out Of It*, and played a sold-out record release show on Columbus Day weekend at then Riley's Rock House in Aurora, Illinois. The cost of recording and releasing the CD totaled $10,000, and if you listen closely to some of those early lyrics, you can learn how they were able to accrue that kind of money while still in high school. The CD, in whose artwork Tanner and I played a minor role because the picture on the CD itself was one I took showing Tanner climbing out of the end of a metal tube we found at a construction site, sold an unheard of 15,000 copies. This was more than any single band the small distribution company had ever handled. This earned the band ample headlining gigs and local acclaim over the coming year as they began to establish a broader fanbase in and around Chicago. This fame then also spread to college campuses in neighboring states like Indiana, Wisconsin and Iowa.

In late 1999 and early 2000, the band recorded *Soapbox Spectacle*, their second EP. Along with 3 to 10, Saturday Night, 23 (God Only Knows), City Lights, Not About Debra and Fred Astaire, the band included the same version of Dumb Pop Song from the previous EP and LP despite reservations about the song becoming a Lucky Boys Confusion cliché. But in January of that year, Chicago radio station Q101 had started playing the song as part of their regular rotation. The positive response was overwhelming, making it impossible for the band to ignore the song's growing importance to their career.

In March of 2000, Lucky Boys Confusion released *Soapbox Spectacle* at about the same time that Q101 released a compilation CD of rising local acts that included the aforementioned Dumb Pop Song. The band now found itself being flown to New York and L.A. and treated to lobster dinners and free drinks by record executives from labels like RCA, Universal and Timebomb. Again the band was cautious, resisting the urge to sign despite their understandable eagerness. This was a courtship ritual wherein the label and the band meet to gauge the other, taking some time to assess the other's potential.

All that LBC will say about their decision to sign with Elektra is that this label seemed the most willing and the most ready to agree to terms that seemed acceptable. In June they signed the dotted line, and in October they were in L.A. recording with producer Howard Benson.

When recording their previous releases in small studios in Chicago, their own best judgment had been their only guide, and that judgment had served them well. When recording with

Elektra, it became apparent that this freedom would be undermined by their producer and Elektra's unseen record executives. They didn't resent their producer, Howard Benson, who went on to record strong albums for bands like My Chemical Romance and Hoobastank, but there were inevitable differences between the band and Benson and the record executives whose suggestions seemed in contrast with those instincts that had carried them through the past years. At some point Lucky Boys Confusion perceived that it was a fight they could not win, and so they compromised more than they would have liked.

When *Throwing the Game* was released in May of 2001, it pleased most of their old fans, who were familiar enough with most of the songs, and garnered them a share of new ones. That same month their single, Fred Astaire, reached number 34 on the Billboard rock charts and entered rotation on FM stations around the country.

This was their big year. This was the year of a tour bus, two television appearances (*The Late Late Show with Craig Kilborn* and HBO's *Reverb*), X-Fest in St. Louis, Buzz Fest in Houston, Q101 Jamboree in Chicago, a tour opening for Eve 6 and a weeklong stint on the Vans Warped tour, to name a few. This was also a year of endless radio interviews, a music video for the song Bossman and even a tour of Japan.

The following year was calmer, spent at home nursing wounds and writing music for the next album. They stayed on their feet by joining several smaller tours, including one with the band Smashmouth, but for the most part they concentrated on writing. This was a crucial year for the band because if Elektra's interest had waned, the label could refuse to record a second album with Lucky Boys Confusion. Elektra was clearly unsure of the band's potential, but they kept writing. By the end of the year LBC had been allotted studio time for their follow-up record, and in January of 2003 they were in Long Beach, California, to record.

For this record they had won the attention of Michael "Miguel" Happoldt, best know for his work with Sublime and The Long Beach Dub All-Stars. The process of recording this album was far different than their first with Elektra. "Miguel didn't necessarily care if I played my part exactly right, but if I played it with feeling," Adam recalled. "It was more relaxed, but it was also more troublesome, in some ways." This, because Elektra seemed altogether indifferent to the band's new record. On the one hand this permitted the band a considerable degree of freedom in the studio, but it was also an inauspicious omen.

If Elektra wasn't poking around to see what the band was doing with its album, the implication was that Elektra wasn't invested in its outcome. And if this was the case, there was no guarantee that the album would ever be released. Eleven hour days in the studio with Miguel thus carried the disappointing prospect of proving a simple exercise in masturbatory self-indulgence. If Elektra pulled out, they also owned all of the recordings and could refuse to release them back to the band.

The album was finished in April, and the band waited. In the meantime they toured with Allister and Bowling for Soup. After a torturous summer of uncertainty, their album *Commitment* was finally released in October of 2003, and with it came another appearance on *The Late Late Show with Craig Kilborn* and a tour with Zebrahead.

The release of *Commitment* compounded the band's frustrations with their label, now affectionately referred to by Joe as "Neglektra." Most distressing to the band was the fact that Elektra tested the album's first single, Hey Driver, in only two markets: Green Bay, Wisconsin, and Denver, Colorado. Despite the fact that the single tested number one in both places and despite positive critical response to the album itself, the label continued to ignore their Chicago quintet.

Ryan, Adam, Stubhy, Joe, Jason. 2006 (photo: Nabil Elderkin)

It was the beginning of the end, and the following summer, as Elektra merged with Atlantic records, Elektra dropped Lucky Boys Confusion from its roster along with most of its other rock acts. The band had been anticipating the news, and with it there came a mingled sense of defeat and newfound freedom.

That summer they toured with Reel Big Fish, and the following fall they headlined their own Suburban Curse tour in continued support of *Commitment*. At the conclusion of this tour they returned home, and thus began their longest stretch of home-life in over five years. Over the following months they compiled a CD of rarities and B-sides, some of them from their former days on Elektra and others from their high school songbook, and in the summer of 2005 they released *The Red Tape Outtakes (Demos and Heartbreaks)*. They released this album independently, employing the same method by which they had released *Growing Out Of It* all those years before.

Rather than a swan song, *The Red Tape Outtakes* seemed more a reflective annotation to their development over the years. The hauntingly infectious harmonies on the disk's concluding song, Le Chanson du Soldat, and its chorus, "This might be the end," spoken by a soldier going off to war, could just as easily have been the band's parting message to their fans at a critical juncture in their career. If it was an end, it held at least the hope of life ahead.

Following a tour in support of *The Red Tape Outtakes*, they returned home again to begin the process of writing and recording the EP *How to Get Out Alive*, which they released in June of 2006 and distributed through Resurrection Records. To celebrate its release the band played five sold-out shows at The Beat Kitchen in Chicago and recorded the second night's performance for release as a live acoustic CD, released the following winter.

On one of those nights of a Lucky Boys Confusion tour when the chaos and debauchery seem fleeting, Adam, Stubhy and I sat at a bar discussing material for the book. As we discussed radio and the band's present and past relationship with it, the name Mancow came up.

"Mancow," Adam repeated. He smiled, seeming to relive several years in his mind all in an instant. "What do you want to know?"

Adam, Jason, Ryan.

Mancow's Morning Madhouse is a nationally syndicated morning radio show broadcasting out of Chicago. The show is an eclectic mix of humor and politics and classic radio theatre that restlessly shifts between these elements with an adolescent attention span, flitting between topics with the frenetic energy of a child's restless fingertips at the keys of a piano.

"Tell me whatever comes to mind," I said.

"Well, he was kind of a prick to us at first," Adam said. "But after we performed and took his harassment well, he actually liked us and he's supported us a lot. We've played live on his show four times. The first time was in the spring of 2000 when he had us in to play Dumb Pop Song. This was back in Mancow's more voyeuristic days, and what I remember and will never forget from that show was looking into the studio and seeing these strippers get totally naked and start fucking each other with dildos.

"That was our first Mancow experience. We played for him again a second and third time, once in support of *Throwing the Game* and then again in support of *Commitment*. Most recently we went in to play The Struggle from *How to Get out*

Alive. That performance illustrates how far we'd come in the six years since that first performance. That morning most of us were functioning on two or three hours of sleep and a lot of liquor. It was in the middle of the same week that we were playing our five consecutive shows at The Beat Kitchen, which essentially turned into a week-long party.

"That morning Joe could hardly stand up, and we had to get one of our friends who worked in an emergency room to hook him up to an IV of interferon so that he could play. I should explain that this friend had 'borrowed' the IV bag a week earlier with the understanding that one of us might potentially need it that week. When we called him that morning, he came and hooked it up to Joe in the parking garage next to the radio station. So for this last Mancow appearance we rolled into the studio jaded, hungover or drunk, and Joe was carrying an IV bag stuck into his wrist so that he could pull himself together enough to play two songs.

"We'd come a long way, and while Mancow had matured, we had sort of degenerated.

Joe. Laughing.

"But the best Mancow experience was when we were in L.A. recording *Commitment*. Our producer, Miguel, took us around to a bunch of different clubs in Hollywood one night. At one point he tried to get us into this Playboy party at a hotel. For some reason they wouldn't let Miguel in, but they let me in because they thought I was Johnny Knoxville. At that time I had black hair and Ray-Ban sunglasses and everything, and I was definitely drunk enough to pass for him. They eventually let Stubhy in because they thought that he was the bass player from No Doubt. There aren't a lot of famous Indians around Hollywood, and so they just assumed that if he wasn't M. Night Shyamalan, he must be the other one.

"I was walking around the party and enjoying myself, and at some point I was standing near this table where there was a guy sitting between all these beautiful girls. I realized that he was being an asshole, making fun of how I looked and trying to impress the girls by trying to be clever and witty. I walked over to his table and stared at him. He stared back at me, trying to act tough while the girls snickered, and then I started taking food off of his plate and stuffing it into my mouth, letting pieces of it fall back onto the table.

"It was an asshole thing to do, and I should've gotten my ass kicked, but just as the guy was getting really pissed off, the girls, who were giggling this whole time, started saying 'No, it's okay! He's from Jackass, that's what he does!' The next thing I knew they were taking pictures with me for some newspaper or magazine or something. I never found out where those pictures were printed, but if I ever meet Johnny Knoxville I guess I owe him an apology for inadvertently impersonating him. Meanwhile this whole time they wouldn't let Miguel in, and he was the only real celebrity of the three of us.

"At some point Stubhy and I went upstairs because we heard that G-Love from G-Love and the Special Sauce was somewhere on the fifth floor. When we got there, we saw Turd from Mancow's show running up and down the hallway shouting and slamming into people, completely drunk. It turned out that Mancow's show was doing a live broadcast from a hotel room above the party. Turd noticed us and recognized us, and he brought us there. They had some Playboy bunnies in the room, and I remember doing body shots off of a Playboy bunny's stomach and playing the bongos on some girl's naked ass during a sing-along. It was fucking amazing.

"When we left, there were all of these limousines out front and all of these really pretentious Hollywood types. Jason came driving up in The Lucky Van with Joe, completely wasted, hanging out of the passenger side window and shouting to us at the top of his lungs. You can imagine the reception he got from everyone else standing around outside, who were trying really hard to fit in and look Hollywood. That was Lucky Boys Confusion's arrival on the scene.

"So I guess that would have to be my favorite Mancow experience," Adam said, lifting his glass and reclining back in his chair.

Stubhy hovered nearby, distracted with something else.

There were now a dozen or so empty glasses and bottles scattered about our table, and a short time later the interview fell apart.

"So what about your relationship with the Olsen twins?" I asked.

"We've never met them, we're just on the soundtrack for their movie *New York Minute*. Our song plays during a chase scene, but I think most of the movie is a chase scene, so I'm not sure which one we're in exactly. I've never seen it."

"And weren't you guys featured in some video game?"

"We weren't featured in it, we just have a song on EA Sports MVP Baseball 2004, I think it is. It's a long title."

"And what other movies were you in?"

"Well, we're not *in* the movies, they just use our songs sometimes. We're in *The Looney Tunes Movie*, during another chase scene, and we're also in the trailer for *Without a Paddle* and—"

"*Without a Paddle*? Sounds like a gay porn title. But I'll bet you're in the chase scene, at least."

Adam sighed. "I'm not sure I want you writing our book anymore."

"You already made me cut out the bestiality and dead hooker stuff. You're *lucky* I'm writing your book."

Adam rose from his seat and walked away. Stubhy was on another phone call and didn't hear.

"Your silence is as good as an admission of guilt!" I shouted after him. "And that goat had a family!"

I turned off the tape recorder and finished the remaining drinks on the table.

Ryan. Loitering.

Small Town Minnesota

EXHIBIT A: Written in smeared black Sharpie upon the fractured bathroom mirror:

I Love Broken Things

EXHIBIT B: Burned into the carpeting near the doorway was the cryptic message:

We become the people we need.

EXHIBIT C: Upon the television screen, drawn with black lipstick, were some obscure and potentially obscene markings. In the center there appeared to be some unintelligible message, written in blood.

EXHIBIT D: Seemingly innocuous enough, the telephone receiver lay upended on the nightstand.

EXHIBIT E: One Queen-size mattress stood on end against the windows. Upon it there had been drawn a large target, also in black. At the foot of the mattress were strewn several bottles, a broken vase, a small potted plant, and one rotting fish.

EXHIBIT F: The wall lamps had been torn from the wall.

EXHIBIT G: One old-fashioned popcorn trolley stood in the center of the room, its popcorn emptied and the kernels spilled upon the carpet. The trolley had been festooned with tampons and the message, written in red lipstick upon its glass, "We're gonna rock around the clock."

EXHIBIT H: Positioned before the popcorn trolley so that it pantomimed a popcorn vendor was an inflatable sex doll, naked, her hands fastened with duct tape to the bar by which the trolley was pushed. Around its neck hung a crudely written sign: "Faith: LBC's #1 Fan." A cigarette had been taped to the inside of her gaping mouth, and there protruded from between her legs an unraveled condom, hanging like a discarded chrysalis in the still air of the room.

EXHIBIT I: "Julie's" telephone number had been scrawled in blue ink on the wall near the bathroom door: 650-741-1396

EXHIBIT J: In the toilet there floated one doll's head. Its red hair had been cut into a Mohawk, and there were strange designs upon its face and a thumbtack through one ear.

EXHIBIT K: While the bathroom mirror still hung above the sink, the mirror in the bedroom had been removed from the wall and lay in a corner, smashed and turned to face the wall.

EXHIBIT L: Scrawled in shaving cream that had soaked into the drywall was the proud proclamation:

The Olsen Twins Pay My Rent.

We were bored.

The afternoon was cloudy, the light dim, and the weather fair. Time dragged on.

The band had completed an uneventful sound check, and Toadie had set up as much of the equipment as he could prior to intermission between opening band Barb Wire and Lucky Boys Confusion's set. Tanner had set up the merchandise table. There were no interviews, no radio station appearances. It was only four in the afternoon, the doors wouldn't open until six-thirty. Lucky Boys Confusion wouldn't take the stage until sometime shortly before ten.

Adam and I sat on a concrete divider behind the venue. We could see three members of the band Barb Wire discussing something a short distance away. One of these was Shelan, Barb Wire's lead singer. Shelan stood nearly seven feet tall, broad shouldered, light Indian skin, dark Indian eyes and a shaved head upon which rested a pair of black sunglasses that cradled his skull like some science-fictionalized tiara.

To his right was a man known affectionately as Chuckles, Barb Wire's bass player. Chuckles was large without being fat, and he possessed the aesthetic qualities of someone whom you might expect to see splashed with war paint and wielding a battle axe as he raised a primeval battle cry alongside William Wallace. But his nature was that of a gentle giant, warm and amicable and always smiling with good natured fondness for life.

The last of the small cluster was Nate, Barb Wire's guitarist. He was dwarfed in comparison to the other two and thin enough to seem excitable by the wind. Similar to the other two, though, he possessed a jovial spirit and a charm that did not go wasted upon the women who called at their dressing room door.

"What was it Keith Richards said about being in a band?" I said to Adam. "Something like 'Hurry up and wait,' right?"

If Adam heard me, he didn't respond.

Shelan approached us. "We're going for drinks," he said.

"Where?" Adam asked.

"Don't know, but it beats staying here."

"Do we have hotels yet?"

"Nope. Apparently our hotels are outside of town."

Adam sighed.

"Come on," Shelan said. "You might as well come."

"I don't want to get drunk before the show," Adam said half-assertively.

"No promises," Shelan said.

He turned to go.

We followed.

I saw the police cruiser before anyone else, but I was laughing too hard to mention it.

To my right in the empty twilight streets was a group of men half singing, half shouting the lyrics to a Social Distortion song.

"*Life goes by so fast!*" they shouted in curious harmony.

To my left paraded Chuckles, followed by Toadie. Following close on Toadie's heels was Nate. They sang along with everyone else, but Chuckles, occasionally forgetting the words to the verses, would periodically interject various non sequiturs that no one seemed to notice.

"I still say Sherman Helmsley is dead," Chuckles said at one point.

"*You only wanna do what you think is right!*"

It was this trio of Chuckles, Toadie and Nate who sent me into the harshest fits of laughter. Chuckles, as drunk and happy as a young rock n' roll Santa Claus, tromped down the street shouting along whenever the song returned to its chorus. Toadie, several feet his junior, followed behind him, taking swigs from a water bottle and spitting the water from between his teeth at the back of Chuckles's hooded sweatshirt, crafting a game in which the unused recesses of Chuckles's hood became a target. This continued unbeknownst to Chuckles, who despite the occasional streams of water that would sometimes skim one of his ears or splash against the back of his head, never seemed to register what was happening behind him.

Meanwhile Nate followed behind Toadie, smoking and ashing his cigarette onto Toadie's head, the ashes becoming fixed amidst the slick gel and hairspray of Toadie's spikes. But Toadie was too engrossed in his own affair to imagine that someone might be getting the best of him.

And before us all, leading this bastard choir, was Stubhy. Smitten with adolescent adrenaline, he would occasionally attack an innocent tree that lined the quiet street or dive into the bushes of the parkway, shouting and laughing as his feet carved an electric choreography in the foliage. Each time Stubhy did this Adam would run up and push him over, sending him sprawling atop more flowers and shrubbery in the process. Stubhy would then chase Adam and tackle him into another cluster of landscaping, their engagement appearing to my eye like a representation of the songwriting struggle, a delicate balance of equal parts abuse and affection.

A car came down the street, and Stubhy ran toward it and shouted, "Stop! I—I need to know what city this is!"

As the car drove past, displaying a shocked and terrified middle-aged woman driver who observed us with confused reproach, Stubhy called after her, "I need to know where we are before we go onstage! I fucking love ... wherever the fuck we are!" Then, thinking of something else, he shook his fist at the departing lights and added, "And where's your daughter? You can't protect her forever!"

Jason splintered off from the group, stopping before a freshly painted fire hydrant. "I've always wanted to do this," he said, smiling as he peed upon it.

"Whatever happened to Mike Patton, anyway?" Chuckles asked.

"Close your eyes and it's passed! Story of my life!"

It occurred to me that we had taken cabs from the concert venue to get to this area of the city, small though the city was, and it was now approaching show time for Barb Wire. But I knew that Adam's mind forever traced a path from one performance to the next, his feet pacing the wooden planks of the stage in constant meditation upon one unbending thought of the show. One could see it behind the creases of his brow and the uneasiness with which he attended to every waking moment of his pedestrian life offstage.

For Adam there was the music, the show and little else.

His internal clock was unerringly set to show times and curtain calls, and even as he seemed possessed by the spirit of our revelry, I sensed that he was consciously leading us back to that night's venue as though drawn by an unrelenting attraction forever commanding his will. So when I saw the police cruiser, I had a moment to think that it might prove a problem.

Fortunately Jason had finished consecrating his lifelong dream several minutes earlier, while the others appeared wholly indifferent to the officer's appearance.

The officer rolled down his window, and the face and figure that appeared behind it was the image of Rod Steiger from *In the Heat of the Night*.

"Excuse me, sirs," he said.

"We're not for sale," Stubhy said.

"Yes, officer?" Adam said, intervening. "Is there a problem?"

The officer looked past Adam to our collection of loud and exuberant drunkenness. "Not sure," he said.

"We're just passing through," Adam said. "On our way to another bar."

"Uh-huh," the officer said, gnawing upon a toothpick, taking his time. "We've had some complaints, is all."

"Complaints?" Adam asked.

"Just some noise about a group of boys running around, terrorizing motorists, peeing on lampposts."

Jason was close enough to hear this and looked discouraged. I thought I heard him mutter, "It wasn't a lamppost."

"Really?" Adam said, sounding incredulous. "And this seems like such a quiet little town."

Behind Adam, the others erupted into a new song, chanting, *"Few times I been around that track so it's not just gonna hap-pen like that!"*

"Said they were dressed all in black," the officer continued. "Loud, obnoxious, maybe vandalizing property. Eleven of them."

"Eleven?" Adam asked.

The officer nodded. "Uh-yep. Eleven, just like yourselves."

"Clearly there are twelve of us, sir. And we'd never do anything to disturb the peace in your endearing little community."

The officer scrutinized Adam's features, searching for the slightest hint of disrespect. Either finding none or deciding to forego any further discussion, he said, gruffly, "I suppose, then, that you can assure me that I won't have any more complaints about eleven *or* twelve boys disturbing that peace? I sure wouldn't like to have to come back around here and find myself talking with the *twelve* of you about it a second time."

From behind them, a familiar voice called out, "What do you think would happen if Dorothy tried to fuck the Scarecrow?"

"We'll tuck ourselves away somewhere where we can be neither seen nor heard," Adam said.

The officer grunted and said, "See that you do."

We hoisted Tanner into the air above our heads and threatened to toss him into a volcano. Drifting along the air from the chaos a voice said, "I heard that if you mix equal parts orange juice concentrate and gasoline it makes napalm."

Toadie set the stage for Lucky Boys Confusion following Barb Wire's performance.

Longtime friends, Shelan and Stubhy have stage presences as unique as they are alike. While Stubhy carries himself with a morose rock star swagger, Shelan is more affable, less intimidating and somehow more candid. His lyrics too are lighter, more fraught with reminiscences and adolescent mischief than Stubhy's, which often have an edge of despair.

Where both share a likeness is in the attention they command from the stage. Both deliver voices unique to rock n' roll, infused with sometimes strange, often hypnotic vocal ranges that drop and catch notes in places and ways that rock n' roll has perhaps never heard. Together they bring a new glamour to the performance that rock n' roll, borne of novelty, is forever eager to uncover.

But this quest for novelty isn't always universally accepted. It fails to account for people's tribal prejudices and common distrust of the new and unfamiliar. One example of this may be found in the corporatization of rock music, a system that relies upon market research conducted by men with calculators in place of ears. Novelty in this arena can be a dangerous and risky gamble for shareholders seeking a safe, sustainable return. But it is not only corporations and major record labels that isolate themselves in the familiar.

People have a tendency to identify themselves with music, and an unwanted change can induce a flux in one's perceived identity. Music is individual and private, but it also unites a community of appreciative and like-minded listeners. A sort of latent territorial protectiveness can thus envelop people as they appropriate a musical style or a band as their own. What is thereafter 'theirs' becomes something to be protected from those to whom that music seemingly doesn't belong.

The pejorative epithet "sell out" thus refers to the perceived dissolution of one's identity, and no identity is more sacred than that of the adolescent struggling to consecrate it for the world. For Lucky Boys Confusion, a band that had relied so much upon the dedication of their loyal fans, the transition to a national stage that invariably ostracized a portion of those early die-hard fans was disheartening.

Lucky Boys Confusion has always been candid and unabashed about their successes and failures, and it would be hard to accuse them of ever having turned their backs on their fans. While there were more than a few Internet message boards peopled with angry and disillusioned kids voicing their resentments over Lucky Boys Confusion's Elektra debut and hit single Fred Astaire, there were plenty of other loyal diehards who felt that their star did not rise high enough.

This struggle to expand their fanbase without alienating longtime fans might have begun in January of 2001, at the start of their relationship with Elektra. Following a sold-out show at Chicago's Metro Theatre that was partly a celebration of the band's recently completed debut album on Elektra, Chicago rock critic Jim DeRogatis described Lucky Boys Confusion's music as a "cipher," saying that "what the group lacks is original thinking."[1]

---

[1] DeRogatis, Jim. "Lucky Boys Confusion at Metro." <u>Chicago Sun Times</u> 15 Jan. 2001: Late Sports Final, Section 2, Features 36.

This particular review, coming when it did, proved a valuable lesson for the band at the start of their national exposure. It was a lesson marked not so much by its accusations, but by a certain fallacy therein.

Behind some of DeRogatis's more acerbic comments were some scant compliments, such as when he said that "the quintet is tight, accomplished and self-assured in the same way that the early Smashing Pumpkins were," or when he conceded that "it's possible ... the still-young band is simply going through its growing pains onstage." But DeRogatis went on to denounce the current crop of "twenty something musicians," namely Lucky Boys Confusion, for having grown up with an alternative radio format and its "incessant hyping of novelty hits and prepackaged rebellion." He described Lucky Boys Confusion as "the regurgitated product of a decade spent listening to programmed alternative hypes" and further stated that, "there's nothing like alternative radio to stunt a boy's growth."[2]

But if DeRogatis wanted to disparage alternative radio, he conveniently omitted himself from its membership. In the early 1990's, Jim DeRogatis co-hosted the radio program *Sound Opinions* on then Chicago alternative radio station Q101 with fellow Chicago rock critic Greg Kot. The program aired late at night and prided itself on playing obscure and upcoming talents as well as precursors to the alternative rock phenomenon.

"I used to listen to every minute of that program every night it was on," Adam said. "That was how I found almost all of my favorite bands that have influenced me over the years."

So when DeRogatis criticized alternative radio for producing a "cipher" like Lucky Boys Confusion, he inadvertently indicted his own influence upon that cipher. What Adam and the band took away from this review was the understanding that critics' opinions, like those of rankled fans, could be equally airless fallacies, and their opinions, positive or otherwise, empty ciphers.

When DeRogatis's own band, Vortis, released a CD of their own some time later, the message was made doubly clear. The CD, hardly listenable even by elitist standards, contained

---

[2] DeRogatis 36

extensive liner notes explaining the concept behind each song and why you, member of the ignorant masses that you are, might not understand why you should like it. This made it easier to appreciate the veiled compliment when DeRogatis named Lucky Boys Confusion's sold out concert at the Metro his number one pick for "Worst Concert of the Year" in 2001.

Friends and fans have come and gone, accolades and criticisms both past and present have left their impression and in their place is something hard, some caustic edge marked by the band's composure and the faded glint in their eyes. They are a band that has relied upon their own self preservational instincts, confronting setbacks and an industry that sometimes operates like a closed fraternity with their own intractable determination, never losing faith in their talent and appeal. They have withstood the hostilities and resentments, their former juvenile faces culled for the hardened resilience of road-weary veterans returned home to a world no longer colored by the innocence of their youth.

But there is another equally powerful force that acts upon them. It is some capricious childhood instinct that in contrast to its cold and pragmatic other makes them somehow more potent and more vital. There is still an endearing happiness that, pulled upon by the weight of experience, tilts the scales higher, ascending new heights just as it plumbs lower depths.

For Lucky Boys Confusion this mix of optimism and tireless persistence has been the key to their continued survival throughout the years.

They are self-titled "Hopeless Dreamers."

No dreams too big.

"There are moments onstage when I'm like, 'fuck yeah, this is the greatest thing in the world,'" Adam said. "And then there are others when I'm thinking, 'what the fuck am I doing? This is pathetic. I should be *doing* something with my life.' There are bands that formed a year ago that are already outselling us. Every night you go through this conflict, but there's also instant reward every night. It's hard to feel like a failure when everyone's buying you drinks and telling you how much your music means to them. You do it as much for them as you do it for yourself."

In Adam's apartment there is a single cactus sitting atop the piano in his living room.

Adam, Ryan. Waiting.

As we sat in a hotel room one night, drinking beer and waiting for the others to return, I mentioned something to Stubhy about a music video I'd recently seen.

"I don't like videos. I don't watch them," he said.

Something in his voice seemed to indicate that this wasn't a matter that I should press. But I was compelled to forego the sentiments of friendship in the interest of gathering material for the book, and so I tried to engage him.

"The Gorillaz videos are good," I said. "So is the Bloc Party video for Helicopters. You like those bands, you might like—"

Stubhy shrugged, and I stopped. His bottom lip was taught, drawn tightly against his teeth.

He scrolled through his iPod, and his demeanor made me uncomfortable, as though I had transgressed some unspoken boundary. Stubhy is notoriously mercurial, and when he wants to, he can be terribly intimidating. Stubhy is charisma stalking across the stage of life, and he possesses an unremitting power to either

204

compel favor or induce dislike and mistrust. If you're leaving and he doesn't wants you to stay, the subtle persuasion of his words and the stern accosting of his eyes will fix you in place; likewise, if he wants you to leave, the same will usher you to the exit.

Several uncomfortable minutes later, he said, "I just hate turning on MTV or Fuse or CVN and seeing them spotlight bands that we've toured with, bands that have opened for *us*."

He found a song and selected it.

"I mean, they're our friends and they make great music. I'm happy for them, and I'm not just saying that. I absolutely mean it." He looked at me then, and it wasn't arrogance in his eyes but an endearing confidence. He laughed despite himself, and added, "And anyway, we're better than them, right? I mean, you can't be in a band and not believe that you're better than nearly everyone else. You need that conviction just to continue."

His cheer faded as he finished, another touch of gloom shading his face. "It's just hard not to feel like it should be us. We've been working so hard at this—it's just hard not to feel like we deserve it, too."

When Lucky Boys Confusion took the stage that night, there was some apparent tension among the band members. Stubhy appeared irritated, more withdrawn than usual, and Adam's casual banter with the audience sounded more caustic than playful. This was no more evident than when he told audience members, "Those of you sitting near the back, I just can't help but wish that you'll die in a fiery car crash on the way home tonight if you don't stand up."

These people stood, but they seemed resentful despite their cheers.

Despite the obvious tension, or perhaps because of it, Lucky Boys Confusion exploded into thundering appeals to their audience, each song starting like the fall of a sledgehammer crashing through stained glass.

When they finished they seemed only marginally pacified, an ominous portent of things to come.

*   *   *

We'd been drinking for some time.

Enervated by the performance, the band members had taken to replenishing their decimated reserves with some, then more, then excessive drinks.

The space backstage soon resembled something like that of a poorly run burlesque. Drinks spilled, voices rose and skimpy costumes draping the smooth surfaces of female forms brandishing affection and coquettish eyes sauntered back and forth with swinging, undulating hips. Here the lights were dim, the rafters and crossbeams overhead like the skeletal remains of some huge, prehistoric leviathan, the dirty and stained backside of the stage curtains a tapestry embossed with revelry.

A brunette proudly exhibited her tattoos and nipple rings to anyone who seemed even slightly interested, while her red-haired friend brandished her beer bottle as though it were little more than a cheap fashion accessory, spilling as much as she managed to drink and lavishing attention upon anyone standing near her.

Meanwhile the blonde stood nearby, attentive and snapping photographs whenever the urge struck her.

From Barb Wire's dressing room one could hear loud shouts and high pitched squeals. Every now and then Nate would emerge, laughing. His eyes would scan the various faces gathered nearest the door before he selected one of the girls and ushered her into their alcove of madness.

A short distance away Ryan had a marker in his hand, and between obscene drawings upon the wall, he would sign the breasts of passing girls who asked him to do so. These girls received either 'REAL' or 'FAKE' written across their chests.

From the LBC dressing room I heard shouts that seemed to betoken a crisis. I decided to investigate, stumbling along a floor that quaked with riot and tempest. Inside, people stood upon chairs and tables that had been pushed against the wall, forming a small ring in the center of the room. They shouted and threw small objects at Toadie and Tanner as they circled each other in the center of the ring.

Standing alone along the outside of the ring, forgotten for the moment, huddled two frightened groupies, clutching each other in terror.

After Toadie lunged at Tanner's legs and toppled him to the floor, they proceeded to grapple with each other, upending tables, scattering food and drinks and miscellaneous furniture. The rest of us, save for the two girls, who continued to hold each other in silent terror, encouraged the combatant of our choice in a rabid frenzy of shouts and threats. Money was exchanged, the victor hotly contested, until at last, when it seemed that no more destruction could be done to a dressing room now thoroughly ransacked and adorned with several additional and unnecessary holes in its walls, we decided to leave.

As we headed outside to the vans, Tanner and Toadie walked with one arm slung about the other's neck, commending each other on a good fight and brushing clumps of food from off of the other's clothes, their former disagreement forgotten.

It was time to find our hotel and a new canvas for our hedonism.

The Lucky Van waited at a stoplight. On the corner was a young couple waiting to cross the street. They appeared to be on a date, still in the awkward and early stages of courtship, and to Ryan's discerning eye they appeared suitable enough targets.

Ryan leaned out of the passenger side window and shouted from the depth of his considerable lungs, "DON'T *LOOK* AT ME!"

The couple started, visibly shaken, and turned with wide-eyed apprehension in Ryan's direction.

Ryan met their timid expressions and said, politely, "What're you ... deaf?"

The light changed and Jason pulled away.

Jason, navigator, tried to follow the Barb Wire van to the hotel, but he made a wrong turn while distracted by something behind him.

The atmosphere inside the van was menacing.

"Give me another beer! I'm thirsty!" Stubhy cried as he crawled with a serpentine fluidity over the backs of the seats, placing his hands upon people's heads and using the purchase to thrust himself toward the rear of the van. "I want to light something on fire!" he added as an afterthought.

"Whose purse is this?" Adam asked, lifting a large black purse onto his lap. He proceeded to sift through its contents, picking out items of make-up and chewing gum and toiletries and daily planners and birth control and dropping them out of the opened window.

"Hey! Ad-*am*," a girl's voice called. "*Stop* it."

Adam shook the purse, looking for something else to toss out of the window, but found only her driver's license and a money clip.

"Here," he said, handing it across several rows. "I cleaned it out for you. You're welcome."

"You shouldn't go through a woman's purse without her permission," Joe said. "A women's purse is an extension of her womb."

"Then that girl's filthy," Adam said. "I can feel legions and pustules developing on my hands already. If I were you I certainly wouldn't go sticking my—"

"*Oww!*" Tanner cried from the rear of the van.

Because the passage from the venue to the hotel via The Lucky Van had been regrettably over-booked, Tanner had been crammed into the small space between the last bench and the rear doors. After reaching this farthest extremity of the van in his search for more beer, Stubhy had wrapped an arm around Tanner's neck and begun nuzzling his fist into the top his head, crying, "This is love! Stop fighting it! Stop fighting it! This is love!"

"Give me your cell phone," Toadie said to one of the girls whose chest read 'Fake.' Opening the phone, Toadie snapped a photograph of Stubhy and Tanner. Then, before the girl realized what he was doing, he filed through her phonebook, found 'Mom Cell' and sent the picture. "Okay, Tanner," Toadie said. "Let's get a picture of your testicles."

"Where the fuck did these bungee cords come from?" someone asked.

"Does anyone have any suggestions about how to get to the hotel?" Jason asked, but he was cut-off as Ryan found another victim on the street and Tanner again began to protest his mistreatment.

We arrived at the Double Tree a short time after Barb Wire, who had already checked in and found their rooms.

When arriving at a hotel from a show it was customary for either Jason or Joe to attend to the front desk while the others waited inside the van. This was one way the band tried to avoid piquing the distrust and apprehension of the locals, whose discerning eyes might otherwise take note of the band's arrival and more closely scrutinize their stay.

Yet after explicit instructions to remain inside the van until business was completed, anticipation and childhood curiosity often triumphed as one by one the remaining band members and their company inevitably disembarked from the van's secure interior. They then scurried furtively and sometimes not so furtively into the night like children emerging from the suffocating confines of parental punishment.

So on this night, when he had seemed to taste the catastrophic potential in the van and had sternly cautioned everyone against leaving prematurely, Jason succeeded only in crossing the threshold of the hotel entrance before all the doors of the the Lucky Van, both at the sides and the rear, simultaneously opened and our troupe of tragic circus clowns spilled clumsily and noisily into the cool night air.

We were visible for a few moments like extraterrestrial aliens tasting the novelty of a new and unfamiliar world before we scattered in various directions. The doors of The Lucky Van were left ajar, the aromas of the van catching the air with the intimation of its own unique biosphere inside. When Jason returned, he paused to gaze disappointedly at the accusation of his lost charges.

By that time the damage had already been done, and had Jason looked behind him in that moment he might have seen the desk attendant speaking on a telephone. A moment later, a curious look on her face, she replaced the receiver and said something to her colleague in an office to her right. Then, picking up a set of keys, she walked out from behind the counter and approached the elevators.

However Jason didn't notice this, and even if he had, it is unlikely that he would have understood its implications. Instead he sighed, closed the standing doors, started the van and drove to the rear of the hotel to find parking.

I recall Adam saying as we left the van, "We're going to Barb Wire's room."

I and several others, I forget who, followed Adam as he somehow managed to trace a path to Barb Wire's room through a maze of winding hallways.

I can recall knocking on the door, I can remember going inside, but I cannot remember much else. What I can say for certain is that everything that transpired inside that room did so in the minutes between Barb Wire checking in to their rooms and Jason finishing checking in to ours.

We were eventually interrupted by a loud knocking at the door, and when Nate went to answer it, he applied the security chain, allowing only the slightest window into the chaos inside.

The woman who had just helped Jason check in to the Lucky Boys rooms stood on the other side of the door. She could see enough to know that her suspicions had been well founded when she saw Stubhy trying to light the cigarette hanging from Faith's mouth and the popcorn cart before which she stood, ostensibly in the area that had once contained a bed.

She asked, with no lack of mounting hysteria, "What is going *on* in there?"

Slurring his words, Nate said, "No room service, thank you." Then, in hoarse whisper, he asked, "Are you an assassin?"

"I'm calling the cops!" she shouted.

"Splendid!" Nate said, becoming cheerful again. "The more the merrier! We don't discriminate."

I saw Adam standing next to Nate during this exchange, struggling to maintain his balance as he peered through the peephole like a mad captain through the periscope of a rogue submarine.

Nate closed the door and advised everyone to dispatch to another room. He then sprayed his beer against the wall and withdrew a marker.

Things had once again become confoundedly boring.

Barb Wire had retreated either to the safety of their van, a bar, or perhaps the open road, where the haunting specter of their last hotel room might not find them.

We had to be quiet, it seemed, because outside the window of Jason's room we could see two police cruisers parked before the main entrance. We were several floors away from the site of our latest revelry, but there was still a sense that we could attract unwanted attention.

Jason had been carrying his luggage into the room when we arrived.

"Where did you guys go?" he asked as we swarmed past him, laughing and toting half-empty cases of beer and various bottles of liquor.

Jason became visibly discouraged as he took a moment to assess the situation. This was especially evident when Toadie, bringing up the rear of our entourage, turned and slammed the door after him. He bolted the door and applied the security chain for added protection and then stood staring out of the peephole, stifling laughter as he waved his hand at everyone, motioning for us to be quiet.

"How could you have possibly caused any trouble in so short—" Jason began, but he stopped himself before finishing. "We better not get kicked out of here."

"Oh, shit!" Toadie hissed. "Be quiet! They're in the hallway!"

"Who?" Jason asked, but Toadie waved his hand again, and the room fell silent.

Several moments later Toadie turned from the peephole. "That bitch just walked by! Can you believe it? She was listening for us!"

"Well, that does it," Joe said. "We're hostages. No one leaves this room for at least an hour."

"Do we have provisions? How many beers do we have?" Ryan asked. The blonde was quiet, apprehensive.

Adam was in the process of counting the beers when he heard this. Regressing to his former high school ways, when supplies of liquor were always at a premium, I watched him quietly slip several bottles under a corner of the bed. His final count was invariably in some contrast to the actual mathematics of supply and consumption, and he always ended up in possession of several more beverages than the rest of us. It had occurred to me that accountancy, his father's preference, would have been a poor fit for Adam if he were employed in a firm with strict prejudices against embezzlement. Adam had once considered politics, where this proclivity might have passed unnoticed and even rewarded, but he had wisely chosen rock n' roll instead. He always considered this a close compromise.

"We have ... sixteen beers," he said.

"And half a bottle of rum and three-quarters of a bottle of vodka," a brunette said.

"And don't forget the Jack Daniels," Toadie added.

"It'll be close," Joe said, "but if we conserve and ration wisely, we should be covered for an hour until we can go find more."

Fifteen minutes later, there was dissention among the ranks.

Adam had grown restless, and Joe, who had defined the parameters of our confinement, now chafed under their guidelines. He wanted to go to his own room with the brunette, but he knew this was impossible. In order to do so he would have to approach the front desk to ask for a new key to his room because the first one had failed to work earlier. To make matters worse, that particular room was across the hall from the one that had apparently become the subject of a police investigation.

Meanwhile Stubhy appeared in need of a walk, and he wanted to see if Barb Wire were still in any of their rooms. This, however, was fraught with various unmentionable risks that made it not worth suggesting.

Thirty minutes later the nervous tension had induced paranoid delusions in a few of the minds of those gathered in the room, and some had started to suspect their neighbor of sabotage. Once, when Toadie had innocently picked up the phone with the idea of ordering a pizza, Joe snapped, "Calling someone?"

"No, I was just—"

"If this were Germany 1943 you'd probably call the S.S. and tell them to check the attic, too, wouldn't you?"

"I was just—"

"Anne Frank is quietly shedding a tear. Get the ropes and duct tape," Joe said.

Ryan rose from his seat.

"Anne Frank's attic isn't in Germany," someone said, but no one paid attention.

Twenty minutes before our internment was scheduled to end, Adam stood and headed for the door.

"I'm going to get a Coke. Fuck off."

We watched him go, and Ryan raised his fist, saying, "Godspeed, Adam!"

Joe watched him depart with baleful eyes. Turning to Ryan, he said, "Judas. Don't think I won't have Stubhy bind your hands and feet again."

Ryan looked to the blonde and winked.

We waited.

Adam found himself retracing his steps more than once through halls that twisted and turned with unnatural contortions. Several times he paused at a floor plan near the elevators in search of a vending machine room. Confident he had deciphered the various symbols and confusing metaphors, he traced the indicated path to disappointment.

At about the time that he was prepared to approach the front desk for clarification, consequences and reprisals be damned, a curious thing happened. While navigating another infuriatingly difficult hallway, a door opened ahead of him.

No one emerged from the room, but he could hear soft voices as he approached and instinctively slowed his step. When he was within a few feet of the room, a voice, pleasant and assured, called his name.

He stopped, confused, and then cautiously advanced another step.

When he was close enough to see inside of the room, he saw a tall woman standing just inside the doorway, smiling. She was dressed in a white t-shirt that embraced her figure in a way that accentuated the intriguing contours of her frame, outlining her breasts and indicating the flat, smooth texture of the stomach underneath. Locks of rich, brown hair cascaded over her shoulders, and farther down her figure the lapidary firmness of her long and slender legs were cloaked in a sleek black fabric that seemed to billow and flutter even in the stillness of the hotel air.

She raised a suggestive eyebrow and stepped aside, her eyes inviting him into the room. Never one to pass up a good invitation, Adam accepted.

Inside he found two more equally impressive women. Both were dressed the same as the first, and their appearance was nearly indistinguishable from her as well. Except that one woman, reclining with a sultry confidence in a chair near the corner, one long and intoxicating leg stretched upon the ottoman before her and the other arched into a formidable peak as her foot rested upon its edge, had rich, black hair that hung in a gentle curtain to either side of the porcelain features of her face.

The third, reposing upon the bed with her back resting against the headboard, had a brilliant mane of red hair that cast an imperial aura about her head.

Had Adam not been preoccupied with other considerations, such as what he had done in a past life to have become so lucky in this one, he might have taken a moment to consider the modest and tranquil lighting of the room—a lighting uncommon to hotel rooms. But Adam was also drunk and still imbued with the thrill of the stage from earlier that night.

He took a seat upon the long dresser and rested one arm on the television beside him.

"We've been wondering about you," said the first, the brunette, closing the door.

"*Waiting* and wondering," added the raven-haired second.

"But patiently," said the red-headed third.

"Some more than others," finished the second.

The first rolled her eyes. "You make me seem so maternal. I was only concerned."

Reaching into his pocket and withdrawing a cigarette, Adam said, "If I'd known, I promise I wouldn't have kept you waiting."

"You didn't know?" asked the second.

"But why not?" asked the third.

Adam lit his cigarette and found the ashtray already waiting on top of the TV.

"I guess I didn't receive the memo," Adam said.

Adam looked at the one seated in the chair. She hadn't moved, and she looked at him with a grave intensity. He looked at the redhead and noticed the same intense expression. The brunette had disappeared into the bathroom around the corner.

The room would not remain steady, and he felt it constantly on the verge of spinning. He made several attempts to assess the present situation and determine who these girls might be.

Were they fans? High-end prostitutes? Sisters? Friends from a previous gig in this town? But none of these solutions really satisfied him. He had neither met nor seen them before. This was an altogether new breed of encounter.

And this led him to consider another, more disconcerting possibility: were they insane? They spoke well, but there was a strange, unbalanced aspect to them, not to mention the fact that they spoke to him as if they knew him and expected him to know them. He had little experience with true madness, and the idea was as frightening as it was intriguing.

"He's trying," said the second.

"Trying what?" asked the third.

"Oh, don't be coy," replied the second.

"You should talk," said the third.

"I don't talk half as much as you," said the second.

"That's why I offered the suggestion," replied the third.

"Don't forget that your hair is already threatening enough," said the second.

"Perhaps. But your tongue does you a disservice," said the third, smiling.

"My tongue services quite well," said the second, also smiling.

"So," Adam interjected, "what're your names?"

"We have some advice for you, Adam," said the third.

"It's good advice," said the second.

"But first we must get you into a state of repair," said the third. "The other twin is arranging that."

The first woman reemerged from around the corner with a small platter of drinks in one hand and in the other a small platter filled with an assortment of chocolate truffles, each cradled in its own piece of dark green crepe paper.

Adam looked at the two trays and exhaled a thick cloud of smoke above his head. The woman approached him and offered first the tray of drinks. Upon it were four glasses of a shape and appearance with which he was unfamiliar. Inside each glass was a small amount of cloudy green liquid that looked a bit like the old Ghostbusters-themed Ecto Cooler Hi-C drink Adam had enjoyed as a child.

He looked from the drinks to the brunette and then again at the others.

"It's okay," said the second. "We'll each be having some."

"You have first choice," said the third. "So you'll know there's nothing sinister afoot."

"Anyway, what's the worst that we could do to you?" asked the second.

"Would you be terribly upset if we took advantage of you?" asked the third.

"We haven't time for that," said the second.

"Unfortunately, I guess," Adam said.

"Take one," said the first, smiling. "You'll like it. It'll give you ... clarity."

Adam chose the glass farthest from him. He lifted the glass to his nose and inhaled the green vapors. It was certainly no Hi-C drink. It had a curious aroma layered with intermingling textures that seemed to dance and speak softly somewhere deep inside of his mind, playfully teasing his expectations with dissembling acts of prestidigitation.

The brunette withdrew the platter of drinks and then offered the tray of truffles.

"I don't really eat much chocolate," Adam said.

"Can you believe it?" said the second.

"Still paranoid," added the third.

"Please entertain us," said the first. "They're unlike anything you've ever had before. They're French."

"When closing the deal, always mention the French," said the second sarcastically. "Men don't care about French chocolates."

"They do when they're offered from women like us," said the third.

"Modesty has never been your virtue," said the second.

"Propriety has never been yours," replied the third.

Adam laughed a little uneasily. He felt a little like he was somehow losing a game of control. His rejections seemed scripted, and the girls seemed aware of that. Even more unsettling was the apparent understanding that he would invariably comply with their requests.

He looked back to the tray and could think of no acceptable reason why he should further refuse the offer, and so he chose one.

The brunette then approached the second, who took first a drink and then a truffle, and the third, who did the same.

"Delicious," said the second, biting into the chocolate.

"Sumptuous," said the third.

"Exquisite," said the first.

"And you?" asked the third, looking at Adam.

Adam bit into the truffle was immediately aware of a foreign presence electrifying his skin. He savored the taste, letting it rest inside of his mouth, and he thought that the sensation was like that of a battery melting upon his tongue.

"I think he likes it," said the second.

"Of course he does," said the third, sounding slightly coquettish, and not for the first time.

"Now you must compliment the flavor with your drink," said the first, raising her glass.

"To Adam," said the third.

"And this evening," said the second.

"And his good company," said the first. She raised her drink to her lips, but her eyes remained fixed on Adam from above the rim of her glass.

Adam brought the glass to his lips. For the first time in a long time he found himself transported, mind and body, away from himself, and he was certain that they had poisoned him.

"I think Adam has succeeded in repairing himself to a more suitable state of composure," said the first.

"What is this stuff?" Adam asked.

"And to think that he thought us mad," said the second.

"To think that he was on his way to get a *Coke*," said the third.

"Can you *imagine*?" said the second.

"Let's to the advice," said the first, taking another sip, still watching Adam. "There isn't much time left."

"Very well," said the third. "You first."

They all turned to Adam and spoke in quick succession.

"Don't overlook the obvious," said the first.

"Don't look back," said the second.

"Don't forget," said the third.

The room fell silent.

Adam looked to each of the girls, anticipating something more. They all looked at him with the same disquieting intensity.

"Oh, and don't smoke so much," added the first.

Adam looked at her.

"*That's* your advice?" he said.

"The last one was more of a suggestion," said the first.

"She's always on about that, you know," said the second.

"She's only concerned," said the third. "It's unhealthy."

"The important stuff was before that," said the second.

"And follow my advice and the rest will follow," said the third.

The phone rang as she finished speaking.

"I'm afraid it's time," said the third.

The first approached him and took the empty glass from his hand. She then ushered him to the door as the phone continued to ring.

"You're not really a chalk outline yet," said the first.

"The kids haven't all gone home," said the second from behind him.

"You have more to do," added the third. "You and the others."

"See?" said the first as Adam stood in the hall, just beyond the threshold. "We're all with you, nonetheless."

"Best!" shouted the two in unison behind her.

"Au revoir," said the first as she closed the door, the gentle click of the latch echoing in the still hallway.

The phone abruptly stopped ringing, and Adam could hear nothing from behind the sealed divide.

The immediate implications of his meeting with the girls faded as Adam walked farther from the room. In the first moments after turning from their room he had been consumed with divining a meaning or some better understanding of who they were. But by the time he had reached the bay of elevators, he could hardly remember from where he had just come and could only vaguely recall some general form their interaction had taken.

Instead Adam found himself once again intent on locating a vending machine and a Coke.

Looking anew at the floor plan mounted on the wall as he waited for his elevator to arrive and finding it now much easier to read its symbols, he discovered a bank of machines on the floor directly below.

He waited for the indicator above the elevator to illuminate the number six. The doors opened, and he boarded and descended one floor.

Without pausing to consider to whom the voices he heard as he exited the elevator car might belong, he rounded the corner with a proud and confident stride.

And then it was too late.

The officer, a short, stocky woman with a displeased grimace chiseled into the stern features of her countenance, turned quickly upon her heels and called to him from down the hall.

"Hey! You!" the officer called. "Come here!"

Adam approached, careful not to give the appearance of hesitation or resistance. He had a moment to regret his decision when he came upon the room before which she was standing.

Another woman stood beside the officer, facing the interior of the room, and she turned to look over her shoulder at Adam's approach. Adam recognized her.

"Is this your room?" the officer demanded, pointing into the remains of a hotel room to her left.

"No," Adam said.

The officer eyed him closely as she spoke to the woman standing beside her.

"Do you recognize him?"

The other woman inspected Adam.

"No. I didn't see him."

"Well, that doesn't necessarily mean he wasn't a part of it," the officer said. Speaking to Adam again, she said, "Let's see some identification."

"What's this all about? Was I one of the ones where?" Adam asked, withdrawing his state identification card from his wallet and handing it to her.

"Where's your room?" the officer asked.

"On the ninth floor," he said, hoping he was right.

"What are you doing down here?"

"I was looking for a vending machine."

"All the way down here? There aren't any vending machines on your own floor?" she asked, her eyes still prying into his. "Or any of the other floors between the ninth and this one, for that matter?"

"None that worked," he said. He didn't think that it would help his cause to explain to this officer that there must surely be functional vending machines somewhere on those intervening floors, though he hadn't been able to locate them in his present state of inebriation.

"They wouldn't take my dollar," he added. "Broken or something."

"Had anything to drink tonight?" the officer asked, inspecting his identification.

"Maybe a cocktail or two," he said. "What happened down here?"

The officer ignored him again, speaking to the other woman. "Illinois ID. I'll have Jake run it when he gets back."

The woman who had discovered the chaos inside of the room looked at Adam again.

"He does look like he could have been one of them," she said.

"Is that what we've come to?" Adam said. "Profiling?"

"Quiet," the officer snapped.

Adam incurred the reprimand and said, "Only trying to help you avoid a lawsuit."

"You know what?" the officer said. Her temper was rising, and this had the effect of putting Adam at ease. "I think you're full of shit. Why don't you come and see for yourself *'what's happened.'*"

Adam looked at her quizzically. "You want me to inspect the room?" he asked. "Isn't that your job?"

The officer snorted dismissively. "I'll bet your memory will just come alive when you look around here and see what you and your little shit-head friends have done."

Adam found himself duly flattered to be recognized for his considerable faculty in this area. He straightened his collar, rolled his shoulders back and adjusted his shirt to its proper fit while patting away any dirt that might have settled upon it. There was confidence in his demeanor, seen most often backstage in the moments before a performance.

He smiled at the officer and approached the doorway to the room he had left less than an hour before. Crossing the threshold he was immediately struck by the powerful stench that greeted him. There was first a smell of beer and cigarettes, which was to be expected, but also something that smelled faintly of burning hair. Mingled with this there was the smell of popcorn and ammonia, and Adam was sure that he could also smell the putrid odor of rotting fish.

The officer was at his side, scrutinizing his reaction, but Adam remained impassive.

"I'll bet it looks different now with all of the lights on," she said.

Adam surveyed the room, trying to piece it all together. He was sure that somewhere there must be a thread that he could follow to some conclusion, some story that could make sense of it all. He was excited by the challenge of finding its sequence of causes and effects.

"Perhaps you'd like to first tell us how the popcorn cart got in here?" the officer said, gesturing toward the popcorn cart and the inflatable doll trying to push it.

"Perhaps she brought it in here on her own," he said, tearing the cigarette from out of Faith's mouth and placing it in his own. His better judgment ruled against lighting it, for now.

"That's pretty funny," the officer said. "Not going to be so funny down at the station."

Adam ignored this and walked over to the mattress that stood against the wall. "Okay, this is key."

"Excuse me?"

"Something like this is clearly the work of band people," he said. "I know the type. I used to play music myself, when I was younger. I mean, who else but band people would do this sort of thing to a hotel room, anyway?"

The officer said nothing.

"Band people love target practice," Adam continued, pointing at the target drawn upon the mattress. "If they're onstage and they get hit with something from the crowd, they want to be able to throw it back and hit the guy who threw it."

Adam inspected the debris scattered about the ground. "The bottles make sense, and even the plant. But I'm not so sure about the fish."

"What about the television?" the officer asked. "Why would you pour beer all over it?"

Adam saw how the officer or the other woman had tilted the television onto the edge of the dresser so that the excess fluid could spill from the ventilation grating in the rear. It looked as though they were draining the oil from an engine, and they had piled towels on the carpet to collect the beer that continued to fall from the set.

Adam nodded understanding. "An offering," he said.

"A *what*?"

"An offering. Whoever this was, they understood that the TV wants too much. It's everywhere in a room like this, telling you who and what to be. It becomes like an omnipresent God. Buy this, become that. So they offered it beer to placate it and to silence it."

The officer grunted.

"If you don't, it can make you into something you don't want to be."

"And the crude drawing on the screen?" she asked, irritated. "What about that?"

Adam shrugged. "I'm not so sure why they did that. But when we were flipping through the channels in our room upstairs, we saw that VH1 is frozen."

"Frozen?"

"Or stuck, anyway. There's something wrong with the transmission, and it's frozen on this picture of a woman in a black dress walking away from a microphone in front of a blue curtain. Her back is to the camera, and she could be a cabaret singer from a Lautrec painting or some actress accepting an award. It's eerie and it's been that way at least since we got here over an hour ago. She doesn't change. I'll bet if you turned on the TV to that station you'd find that whatever's drawn on the screen will somehow fit with that image."

"We can't turn it on. It's probably broken what with all of the beer that's been spilled into it."

"Anyway, that's my guess," Adam said.

"Your guess, huh?" the officer said. "Seem to know a lot for someone who wasn't here."

"I'm just doing what you asked me to do. All I want is a Coke," Adam said. "You wanted me to speculate."

"There's a message burned into the carpeting near the doorway. You stepped over it when you came in. What's behind that? And don't bother feeding me any more bullshit about it being some sort of cultural statement. You may as well start telling me the truth."

"What's it say?" he asked.

"Go and look! And when you're done you can tell me how you intend to explain the bathroom."

Adam walked over to the doorway and read the message 'We become the people we need.' He then stepped into the bathroom and read the statement on the bathroom mirror.

Before leaving he also noted the baby doll's head in the toilet, which surprised him a little.

He emerged from the bathroom and, mumbling a little to himself, started to inspect the lamps that hung precariously by their wiring from the wall.

"Well?" the officer said, her impatience returning.

"See, this is your trademark rock n' roll vandalism here," he said, holding one of the lamps. "These lights make them nervous. The light is too harsh unless it's stage lighting—that's when they want to be seen, that's the performance. Offstage, the light becomes a reminder and an accusation. These lights don't show a crowd or anything they want. They just highlight a crappy hotel room, the girl for the night hanging off of their arm and a reflection that makes them uncomfortable. So with a fixture like this, they just bend the lights down and twist them off. I've seen worse."

"You've seen worse? Those things cost money, just like the mirrors," she said, gesturing toward the smashed pieces in the corner. "Money you and your friends will have to pay to replace them."

"Well, the smashed mirrors should be expected, shouldn't they?" he said with some finality as he dismissively waved his hand in their direction. "They hide from the light to hide from their reflection in mirrors that lie because they don't tell them the truths they want to hear. So they lie to them, like we all do, by splashing on cosmetics, hair dye, top hats and suits to cover and to fill the insecurities. They become ..."

Adam trailed off and turned back to Faith pushing the popcorn cart.

"Faith here is the girl they were about to sacrifice to the television," he said. "And the doll's head in the toilet? They pulled it from her womb in a bloodletting ceremony signifying the birth of our culture. The toilet was the baptismal fount. Then they left it, abandoned and drowned. They were on to the next moment, the next excitement."

"The next excitement like Julie?" the officer asked. "Her number is on the wall. Should we call her? Will she know who you are?"

Adam smiled.

"Well, Julie. Who is she? She's the same girl who goes to every concert looking to glom onto something. She's lost, looking for membership. She wants to be a part of something, wants to get backstage access, wants to feel appreciated and wanted. She's cute, even beautiful, but she doesn't really know that. At least, she doesn't really believe it. She only knows that men react to her, but she doesn't consider that beauty. When she wants to come back to the hotel, they don't tell her no. The band invites her. They get her number," he said, pointing to the wall.

"They know why they're asking her here, and she does too. You might think they're exploiting her, but Julie finds at least a sliver of satisfaction—no more or less than the band members who spend the night with her. She might feel good, she might even find what she was looking for. Part of what she's looking for is validation and attention to prove that she isn't invisible. She lives in a world in which she's constantly being bumped into by her parents and her peers and adults, overlooked and unheard. She wants to convince herself that she exists. Today, *tonight*, she adjusts her eyes to accommodate others' vision, and she drinks enough to be okay with that.

"Maybe it's even successful. Until the morning. Then she becomes just another Julie, a number, maybe a photograph here or there, but no real sense of who or what she was. But that's not the band's fault. They have to leave for the next town, and maybe they understand her a little better than most because they can, in some way, identify with her. She's someone with no sense of self outside of others. They're both sort of adrift on this sea of objectification and isolation."

He paused, trailing off.

And Adam then heard a new voice speaking outside of the room. The voice undoubtedly belonged to the second officer, the Jake referred to earlier. The voice was deep and rough like a gravel road under a stagecoach wheel. It was distinct, and Adam recalled it immediately. A pall came over his face, and he tensed.

The voice remained outside.

"I need to step outside and ask my partner to run your information," the officer said, stepping outside to give the officer Adam's identification card. To Adam's relief and utter astonishment, Jake left without entering the room. He was going back downstairs to his squad car to run the information without and retrieve some paperwork.

Adam felt a renewed sense of hope as Jake's footsteps departed. The picture on his ID was several years old, and since that time his appearance had undergone numerous overhauls and revisions. It was therefore possible that if he could remain out of sight of Jake, he might yet escape his recognition.

"You still haven't told me about this message in the carpet," the officer said, glancing down as she reentered the room. "You might as well keep talking until we confirm that the room is in your name and we run your info."

Adam smiled and briefly met her eyes.

"'We become the people we need,'" he said, looking now at the writing in the carpet. "This belongs above the mantel of the world. Most people believe this implies that we become heroes in times of need. We'll save the victim at our own risk, we'll tie the tourniquet and pull the child from the flaming wreckage. But most of the time we become the person we need to get what we want from others. We market ourselves and wear our identity like a fashion accessory, and we become something for others for ourselves. You and I are doing it right now."

"Jesus Christ," she said, looking at her watch. "I'm sorry I asked."

"Think about the people who did this," he continued, ignoring her. "Rock n' roll people. They're constantly becoming people for others. They live a life almost entirely in the service of others, and these others paint them with their own desires, their own design of who they want their rock stars to be. And rock stars become those people not only because they appreciate the attention, but because they need it to succeed and to thrive. It's a life of service not just to others, but also to themselves, and it can be dangerous because they can lose something in the process.

"Maybe they lose the idea of who they were before, which was closer to home. The road is adventure, but it's also a place where you can become ... transparent. People tend to define themselves in habit and ritual. Then, on the road, the stage is ritual, and the hotel is habit."

Adam paused again and looked around the room. "Sometimes, they rebel."

He looked at the officer, who pretended not to be listening.

"Maybe they do this because it's expected of them," he continued. "Ever since the Rolling Stones were photographed sitting on a hotel bed with their boots on, rock n' roll became the image of property destruction, among other things. So part of it's a learned behavior. If you're part of a rock n' roll band, you need the crazy hotel stories to tell your friends and to fuel the fascination of your fans."

He surveyed the entirety of the room and fumbled with the cigarette in his hand. He felt a curious sense of relief that was both disconcerting and strangely exhilarating. He felt as though he had revealed too much, and he felt naked and vulnerable.

"You know what I think?" the officer asked.

"No, I don't."

"I think it's just a bunch of spoiled brats with no sense of responsibility and a total disregard for other people's property," she said.

Adam regarded her solemnly. "I can't argue with that," he said. "I might even agree with you, someday."

A stillness then enveloped them, and the Double Tree assistant manager returned, entering the room with a clipboard laden with various triplicate forms. She began filling them out, periodically raising her head to look about the room. Her face was pocked with acne scars vainly concealed beneath a thick caking of cosmetics. She only looked at Adam once.

Then Adam heard the elevator bell toll down the hall. A moment later he could hear the distinct, raspy murmurings of a walkie talkie drawing near.

"Excuse me," Adam said as the officer crouched down to inspect a corner of the room with new interest. "You mind if I use the bathroom?"

The woman rose and looked at him, not wanting to appear too amenable. She nodded, biting her lip.

Adam closed the bathroom door behind him just as Jake entered the room.

He waited.

Jake spoke to the woman officer and indicated that Adam's record was, in fact, clean, and the assistant manager confirmed that the room was not in his name.

Adam smiled.

Then Jake asked his partner where he was, and Adam's smile faded. Adam knew that if Jake intended to remain in the room, he was finished. He would emerge from the bathroom, Jake would see him, and then the real questions would begin, and it would become a long night for all of them.

The female officer told Jake that he was in the bathroom, and Jake said that he would wait. He then asked his partner what Adam had told her. She explained that he had told her an unending litany of lies and evasions but nothing that could place him in the room at the time. Both officers, Adam thought, sounded disinterested.

Adam heard Jake say that he would try speaking with him, that perhaps he could do a better job of getting Adam to admit to something. Adam wondered how this remark must have registered with his partner.

Adam flushed the toilet. He went to the sink where now sat the baby doll's head, staring absently into space, and turned on the water. He looked at himself in the mirror and saw his distorted reflection in the spaces between the words written there. He splashed his face with cold water, his countenance defeated. 'I'm afraid it's time,' he heard a voice say.

Over the rush of water he heard a voice speaking to Jake from the walkie talkie clipped to his shirt. Jake responded with his location, and following another distorted stream of words that sounded like an address and some code numbers, Adam heard Jake say that he would be able to respond to the scene within a matter of minutes.

Adam then heard Jake tell his partner that he would have to leave the rest of the matter up to her because he was leaving to respond to a domestic dispute nearby. Adam heard them exchange some brief words, the woman sounding envious that he should be able to leave before her, and Adam heard Jake depart, the static and distortion of his walkie talkie fading down the hallway.

Adam waited a few moments for good measure and emerged from the bathroom. He looked around in feigned surprise and asked, "Where's the officer with my ID?"

She handed him his card and said, "It checked out. You're free to go."

"Is that all?" Adam asked. "Are you sure?"

"Don't push your luck," she said.

Adam stepped from the room without saying goodbye and offered the assistant manager one last look before turning and walking languidly toward the vending machines he believed he would find at the end of the hall.

As he drew near the gentle hum of machines, he withdrew a dollar.

Then he stopped.

Two machines stood idling in the harsh fluorescent light. The one was a vending machine of cookies and chips and cellophane sandwiches. The other, red, blue and white with blue lettering, read 'Pepsi.'

He stared for a moment in disbelief. Then he put the dollar back into his wallet and walked away.

How to Get Out Alive

That summer Lucky Boys Confusion played 44 shows in two months for more than 17,000 fans.

It was to be one of their last national tours.

Somewhere between cities, along the vast network of the American interstate highway system, the members of Lucky Boys Confusion decided to stop making more music. They returned to Chicago and pursued different musical paths.

I returned home and wrote a book that attempted to capture the thrill and excitement of life on the road with Lucky Boys Confusion. I was fortunate to have had the opportunity to experience that life on the road with them, if only briefly, before it passed, and I have tried to bring those experiences and a sense of that thrill to these pages. My success or failure is in some ways irrelevant to me—the fact that I tried my best and that I am left with the memories is what matters most.

But Lucky Boys Confusion only agreed to stop making *more* music, which is to say that they are still kicking and thrashing their way across stages throughout Chicago and the Midwest. Whoever doubts the praises that appear throughout the preceding pages may yet see them play with the same earnest vitality that they have brought to every show since their first in 1997.

Their rock n' roll mystery train still thrums, still races across the worn planks of the stage that is their home as Lucky

Boys Confusion drifts into a slow, building crescendo, the drums and amplified guitars pounding into the audience's chests, reverberating inside the cavernous hollows of their isolation and massaging their desperation with teeth-rattling excitement. It is then that one can perceive the train thundering onstage, one green light, one red, one scathing electrified chorus echoing in its wake.

A sea of feet soon quiver, soon caper a little ideogram upon the sticky floorboards, moving to the syncopated rhythms enveloping each and every one in a riotous intensity as the chorus of voices reach a fevered and frenzied tenor, screaming appreciation, acceptance, and rapture.

This is the performance, the identity and the release.

This is the show.

Closing Arguments:

Author's Afterword

I wrote this book over the span of three years, between the ages of 23 and 26. For several reasons which coincided with Lucky Boys Confusion's 15th anniversary, I returned to my text at the age of 32 with the idea of revising it one last time. I wanted to address the various mistakes and errors in the text that had become a resounding chorus of recriminations both wounding my ego and demanding attention since its first publication. By this time I had no illusions about sculpting the book into anything approximating a formidable literary achievement. I simply haven't that kind of talent, much less the time required to compensate for this deficiency. Instead I simply wanted to revise my text into something respectable enough that I wouldn't have to deny my association with it—a denial that is rather difficult when one's name is listed as the sole author.

As I plodded through the task of reading, editing, then re-reading and editing the text again, I found myself more of a stranger to it than ever before. I remember well the long process of first writing this book, including the various apartments I lived in (there were three, all of them in downtown Chicago) as well as the several Starbucks cafes where I would sit for many hours in order to get out of those often dreary, sometimes vermin infested apartments. It's a familiar cliché, that of the trendy yuppie or hipster who, imagining himself a writer, sits for hours in a Starbucks while he writes either a shitty novel or a hackneyed screenplay, and I certainly filled well that role. But I make no excuses for having worked in this way. I loved being out in the city of Chicago, in the West Loop and Old Town and Little Italy, my headphones enveloping me in Bloc Party, Nine Inch Nails and Mars Volta while I wrote of my adventures with Lucky Boys Confusion. These were my favorite bands to listen to as I tried desperately to sculpt these stories and my writing into something good enough to be sold to Lucky Boys Confusion fans.

My relationship to the text today is somewhat different than it was then, and a few thoughts come to mind on the occasion of its reissue. I recall wanting to represent a true, unabashed account of guys—twenty-something year old guys—marauding through America on a filthy, debauched rock n' roll tour. Something akin to a frat house on wheels, as Adam once described it, though without the roofies, Ed Hardy t-shirts and latent homophobia of most college fraternities. If my text may be described as having succeeded in at least one small respect, this may be it, as the book is saturated with the riotous bad behavior expected of a young touring rock band.

But there is a part of the 32 year old author who reads some passages, particularly those that unnecessarily malign women on account of their age and appearance, as lacking in any satirical or literary merit. At times I feel these passages come across instead as inept and unsophisticated, and I hope that readers will regard these moments more as a reflection of the callow 24 year old who wrote them than of the 32 year old whose name is yet attached to them.

For what it's worth, I should note that I was aware of these issues when I first wrote the book. In order to mitigate the effect of these offenses, the book begins and ends with what I perceived as strong female characters (albeit strong female characters who yet fit into Lucky Boys Confusion's sordid rock n' roll world). These women seem to exert some measure of power and control over the males in their presence. Characters like Rosemary in Cleveland and the three weird sisters in Small Town Minnesota were thus intended to qualify the other less flattering portraits of women that fill the rest of the book. Adam's discourse with the police officer near the book's end represents a last attempt to portray the men of Lucky Boys Confusion as equally the victims of the chaos and identity confusion as the groupies at their side.

Today part of me believes that this design failed to meet my original expectations. Perhaps this is because so many other designs of the book also failed or because I simply lack the requisite talent to successfully execute these complex objectives. What remains is a book that tried its best to capture the voice, the violence and the vitality of Lucky Boys Confusion in all of its inherently erratic splendor. And this may ultimately constitute my greatest defense of the book: that despite its literary failures, it remains true to its subject by way of those failures. The book is sometimes disjointed, uneven and bombastic, it is at times too self-aware and at other times too unrestrained. In this way it is a reflection of the erratic immaturity and unabashed hubris of a young writer, and it mirrors the erratic immaturity and unabashed hubris of its young songwriter/performer subjects.

This edition reflects many revisions and excisions that correct a number of issues which too often detracted from the readability of the first edition. To that end I have corralled some of those younger impulses that resulted in poorly executed literary flourishes. Not all of the issues have been corrected, but perhaps I have persuaded enough of them to recede into the white spaces and background noise so as to be less noticeable and less distracting from the book's better traits.

I should add that I do still love hitting the road with the guys. Combing through my text with an eye for improvement may make for a cruel taskmaster, but there are still pleasant surprises along the way—sentences that are just right, characters that make me laugh and plot twists I'd forgotten. It may not be the expert text I had always wanted or had imagined it to have somehow become in the intervening years since its first publication, but this book is still a good friend with whom I enjoy spending time. I can only hope that readers find some trace of that enjoyment in their own reading. This is ultimately only a hope, as any writer knows, and little more.

One final note.

Like everyone else, I am heartbroken over the loss of Joe Sell. I don't want to say much about this here because I don't want anything I say to overshadow the words of those who knew Joe far better than me. Furthermore Joe was never a tremendous fan of this book. Though this fact has always saddened me, I've always understood and respected his reasons.

It's a well established fact that a writer should never write about one's friends or family, and for this reason: at some point you will almost certainly say something that they will not like, and even more unfortunately, you may say something that will inadvertently hurt them. I have always hoped that if I erred on either of these points, I did so only in violation of the first and not the second, particularly with respect to Joe and everyone in the band. This is my hope now more than ever. I never intended to betray either the trust or friendship of those I wrote about for this book, and I never wanted any description or portrait to leave them feeling insulted. I only wanted to have fun and to bring their story to life through the various vignettes and occasional exaggerations that appear in the preceding pages.

The disclaimer that opens this book was designed to clarify this intent, and it was something that a few of the band members had required that I write and include before they would give their consent for the book's final publication. I fully appreciated then and still appreciate now their relative discomfort with the finished product, as this book is admittedly experimental in much of its composition. Creative nonfiction doesn't always generate broad appeal, and it is even less appealing when in the hands of a somewhat less than capable writer.

Of course it's possible that Joe was neither upset with nor offended by anything I said but simply didn't like the style in which I had said it. Bookish and critical as he was, Joe may have been unable to see past the book's overall deficiencies. If this is the case, I can only defer to his judgment and hope that Joe may forgive me my mistakes. May he forgive me further if I have not yet repaired them to a condition befitting his approval.

I look forward to discussing it with him further someday. He and I and all of the great authors with whom he is now undoubtedly sharing a beer in some fantastic all-star book club in the sky. His opinion has always meant a lot to me, and even if I never attain it, I still have the desire to earn his full approval for something I write. Someday he may tell me, honestly, if I ever have.

There's still time, and I'm still trying.

Derek Brezette
10/26/12

CPSIA information can be obtained at www.ICGtesting.com
Printed in the USA
LVOW12s0054270713

344685LV00012B/314/P